Check and test

Maths

Rob Kearsley Bullen

Published by BBC Educational Publishing,
BBC White City, 201 Wood Lane, London W12 7TS.

First published 2001   Reprinted 2002 , 2003

© Rob Kearsley Bullen/BBC Worldwide (Educational Publishing), 2001. All rights reserved.

ISBN 0 563 54445 7

No part of this publication may be reproduced, stored in any form or by any means
mechanical, electronic, recording or otherwise without prior permission of the publisher.

Colour reproduction by Spectrum Colour, England

Printed and bound by Poligrafico Dehoniano, Italy

Contents

Shape and space

Graphs

Handling data

Probability

Answers

About GCSE Bitesize

GCSE Bitesize is a revision service designed to help you achieve success in your exams with books, television programmes and a website, which can be found at **www.bbc.co.uk/education/revision**. It's called Bitesize because it breaks revision into bite-sized chunks to make it easier to learn.

How to use this book

This book explains and tests the **100 essential things** you need to know to succeed in GCSE Maths. It provides:

- the key vocabulary you need in the 'Check the facts' section
- activities to test your understanding in the 'Test yourself' section.

Use this book to check your understanding of GCSE Maths. If you can prove to yourself that you're confident with these key ideas, you'll know that you're on track with your learning.

You can use this book to test yourself:

- during your GCSE course
- at the end of the course during revision.

As you revise, you can use *Check and Test* in several ways:

- as a summary of the essential information on each of the 100 topics to help you revise those areas
- to check your revision progress: test yourself to see which topics you're confident with
- to keep track and plan your time:
  - you know how much time you have left to revise in
  - you know how many topics you need to cover
  - aim to check and test a set number of topics each time you revise.

There are three levels of Maths examinations: Foundation Tier, Intermediate Tier and Higher Tier. This book covers all of these levels and also the new short courses. The h symbol in this book indicates the information and questions that only need to be covered by Higher Level entrants. Your school or college will determine which tier is best for you, and your teacher will usually discuss this with you before your entry is sent to the board.

GCSE Bitesize revision materials

There's nothing like variety for making revision more interesting, and covering a topic from several different angles is an ideal way to make it stick in your head. There are lots of GCSE Bitesize Revision materials in different media, so take take your choice and make learning enjoyable.

GCSE Bitesize Revision: Maths is a book which contains the key information and skills you need to revise, plus lots of tips and practice questions to help you improve your results. GCSE Bitesize Revision: Maths ISBN: 0 563 46119 5

The GCSE Bitesize Revision: Maths website provides even more explanation and practice to help you revise. It can be found at **www.bbc.co.uk/education/revision**

Good luck!

Check the facts

You can **add** or **subtract** numbers in columns, or in your head if they're not too big.

You may be asked to **multiply** numbers, showing all your working. You can work in columns or using a grid method.

There are several ways to **divide** numbers, but the standard 'short' and 'long' methods are fast and efficient.

Remember that when operations are mixed up, they have to be done in the right order. You can remember the order with the 'word' BoDMAS. This means **brackets**, then **powers/roots**, then **divide/multiply**, then **add/subtract**.

> **So $3 + 2 \times 4^2 = 3 + 2 \times 16 = 3 + 32 = 35$,**
> **But $(3 + 2) \times 4^2 = 5 \times 16 = 80$.**

to add 9	add 10, then subtract 1
to subtract 9	subtract 10, then add 1
to add 99	add 100, then subtract 1
to multiply/divide by 10, 100, 1000	move the digits in the number left/right 1, 2 or 3 places, keeping the decimal point fixed
to multiply by 9	multiply by 10, then subtract the original number
to multiply by 5	multiply by 10, then halve the answer
to multiply by 4	double, then double again
to divide by 5	double, then divide by 10

Test yourself

1 Use any shortcuts you can think of to work these out. Do them mentally or with just a few jottings.

a) $915 + 9$ b) $62 + 99$ c) $1067 - 9$
d) $235 - 90$ e) 45.6×100 f) $84 \div 10$
g) 61×9 h) 240×5 i) 521×4
j) $2135 \div 5$ k) 66×25 l) $4500 \div 500$

2 Use written methods to do these.

a) $2126 + 3489$ b) $12\,760 - 8785$ c) 477×8
d) $6254 \div 7$ e) 3084×52 f) $21\,576 \div 31$

Check the facts

There are several different types of number:

- **Natural numbers** are the numbers you count with: 1, 2, 3, 4 . . .
- **Integers** are positive and negative whole numbers: . . .–2, –1, 0, 1, 2 . . .
- **Rational numbers** include the integers and also fractions. Numbers like $-\frac{1}{2}$, 0.3333 . . . and 1.8 are rational.
- **Irrational numbers** can't be written as fractions. Numbers like $\sqrt{2}$, $\sqrt[3]{10}$, and π are irrational.

   Warning! Not all roots are irrational, for example, $\sqrt{4} = 2$, which is an integer.

There are several special kinds of integer:

- **Even numbers** are divisible by 2.
- **Odd numbers** leave a remainder when divided by 2.
- **Square numbers** are the squares of the natural numbers: $1^2 = \mathbf{1}$, $2^2 = \mathbf{4}$, $3^2 = \mathbf{9}$, $4^2 = \mathbf{16}$, and so on.
- **Cube** numbers are the cubes of the natural numbers: $1^3 = \mathbf{1}$, $2^3 = \mathbf{8}$, $3^2 = \mathbf{27}$, $4^2 = \mathbf{64}$, and so on.
- **Prime** numbers can't be divided by anything except themselves and 1: 2, 3, 5, 7, 11 . . . are prime.

Test yourself

$$\sqrt[5]{10} \quad -0.5 \quad 1\tfrac{1}{2} \quad 0.09 \quad \sqrt{6} \quad \tfrac{1}{400} \quad 6$$
$$0.3 \quad 12.5 \quad \pi \quad \tfrac{75}{4} \quad 1.25$$
$$0.6 \quad \tfrac{1}{5} \quad \sqrt[3]{1000} \quad \tfrac{7}{10} \quad 125 \quad -19 \quad 1\,000\,000$$
$$-\sqrt{12}$$

1 From the cloud, write down all the . . .
   a) natural numbers, b) rational numbers, c) integers, d) irrational numbers.

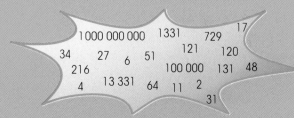

1 000 000 000   1331   729   17
34   27   6   51   121   120
216   100 000   131   48
4   13 331   64   11   2
31

2 From the shape, write down all the . . .
   a) square numbers, b) odd numbers, c) prime numbers, d) cube numbers.

Numbers and calculations

BBC GCSE Check and Test: Maths

Check the facts

Powers are made by multiplying a number by itself repeatedly.
So $2^4 = 2 \times 2 \times 2 \times 2 = 16$, $5^3 = 5 \times 5 \times 5 = 125$.

Powers use a large number (the **base**) and a small number written up and to the right (the **index**). The index tells you how many of the base to multiply.

Some powers have special names. 10^2 is 'ten **squared**'. 6^3 is 'six **cubed**'.

Your calculator power key may look like one of these:

Some calculators have special keys for squaring x^2.

Remember: any number to the first power is just the number
(e.g. $10^1 = 10$). Any number to the zeroth power is 1 (e.g. $5^0 = 1$).

Roots are the opposite or inverse of powers.

$3^2 = 9$. 9 'unsquared' is 3. This is called the **square root** of 9 and is written $\sqrt{9} = 3$

$7^3 = 343$. 343 'uncubed' is 7. This is called the **cube root** of 343 and is written $\sqrt[3]{343} = 7$

Your calculator should have a root key. It may look like one of these: $y^{\frac{1}{x}}$ $x^{\frac{1}{y}}$ $\sqrt[x]{y}$

Some calculators have special keys for square roots .

Test yourself

1 Work out these powers. Check your answers using roots.
   a) 5^5 b) 100^3 c) 35^2 d) 1.5^4 e) $(-8)^2$

2 Find these roots. Round to 3 d.p. if necessary. Check your answers using powers.
   a) $\sqrt{729}$ b) $\sqrt[3]{729}$ c) $\sqrt{1.44}$ d) $\sqrt[6]{25}$ e) $\sqrt[3]{-64}$

3 Write <, > or = in place of the question marks.
   a) $10^3 ? 2^{10}$ b) $\sqrt{625} ? 5^2$ c) $\sqrt[4]{100} ? \sqrt[3]{31}$
   d) $2.1^5 ? 2.5^4$ e) $(-6)^2 ? 6^2$

4 Find x.
   a) $2^x = 4096$ b) $\sqrt[x]{8000} = 20$ c) $1^x = 1$

5 Evaluate these. Round to 3 d.p. if necessary.
   a) $2^3 \times 3^2$ b) $(2^5)^3$ c) $\sqrt[3]{\dfrac{2^9}{5^6}}$

Check the facts

When you **multiply** two powers that have the same base, there is a simple rule for finding the answer. Just **add** the indices.

For example, $2^5 \times 2^4 = 32 \times 16 = 512 = 2^9$.

$$5 + 4 \qquad\qquad\qquad = 9.$$

So $5^2 \times 5^3 = 5^5$. *Check:* $25 \times 125 = 3125$ ✔

This also works with algebra terms: $x^7 \times x^4 = x^{11}$.

To **divide** powers, **subtract** the indices.

For example, $3^6 \div 3^2 = 729 \div 9 = 81 = 3^4$.

$$6 - 2 \qquad\qquad\qquad = 4.$$

So $10^7 \div 10^4 = 10^3$. *Check:* $10\,000\,000 \div 10\,000 = 1000$ ✔

This also works with algebra terms: $\dfrac{p^8}{p^3} = p^5$

> **Warning! You can't do this if the powers have different bases. There's no quick way to work out $2^6 \times 6^2$, for example.**

Test yourself

1 Write the answers in index form. Check your answers by multiplying the numbers.
a) $2^4 \times 2^3$
b) $5^2 \times 5^2$
c) $7^3 \times 7^2$
d) $10^4 \times 10^5$
e) $8^2 \times 8^4$

2 Write the answers in index form. Check your answers by dividing the numbers.
a) $6^4 \div 6^2$
b) $9^4 \div 9^3$
c) $20^4 \div 20^1$
d) $\dfrac{3^8}{3^2}$
e) $\dfrac{4^{10}}{4^4}$

3 Find n. Check your answers by multiplying or dividing.
a) $5^2 \times 5^n = 5^7$
b) $9^4 \div 9^n = 9^4$
c) $10^n \times 10^6 = 10^8$
d) $50^n \div 50^3 = 50^2$
e) $\dfrac{2^{12}}{2^n} = 2^1$

4 Write the answers in index form.
a) $x^4 \times x^3$
b) $\dfrac{c^6}{c^2}$
c) $p^2 p^3$
d) $\dfrac{n^{12}}{n^5}$
e) $n^a \times n^b$

Check the facts

Negative indices give reciprocals.

For example, $2^{-1} = \frac{1}{2}$. Similarly,

$$2^{-2} = \frac{1}{2^2} = \frac{1}{4} \quad 2^{-3} = \frac{1}{2^3} = \frac{1}{8} \quad 2^{-4} = \frac{1}{2^4} = \frac{1}{16}, \text{ etc.}$$

Fractional indices mean **roots**.

For example, using the index rule for multiplication,

So $9^{\frac{1}{2}} = 3 = \sqrt{9}$ Similarly, $10^{\frac{1}{3}} = \sqrt[3]{10}$ and $2^{\frac{1}{5}} = \sqrt[5]{2}$

h Fractional indices that have numerator greater than 1 mean a combination of powers and roots. The denominator is the root and the numerator is the power.

Examples:

$$27^{\frac{2}{3}} = \sqrt[3]{27^2} \text{ or } \left(\sqrt[3]{27}\right)^2 = 9; \ 32^{\frac{3}{5}} = \sqrt[5]{32^3} \text{ or } \left(\sqrt[5]{32}\right)^3 = 8$$

Just to make things even more complicated, you can have negative fractional indices!

Examples:

$$16^{-\frac{1}{4}} = \frac{1}{\sqrt[4]{16}} = \frac{1}{2}; \ 1000^{-\frac{2}{3}} = \frac{1}{\sqrt[3]{1000^2}} = \frac{1}{100}$$

Test yourself

1 Write these negative indices as fractions.
a) 2^{-5} b) 10^{-2} c) 3^{-3} d) 5^{-1}

2 Evaluate these negative indices. Give answers to 3 s.f. where necessary.
a) 10^{-6} b) 4^{-2} c) 2^{-8} d) 3^{-4}

3 Write these fractional indices as roots.
a) $5^{\frac{1}{2}}$ b) $100^{\frac{1}{5}}$ c) $2^{\frac{1}{3}}$ d) $8^{\frac{1}{9}}$

4 Evaluate these fractional indices. Give answers to 3 s.f. where necessary.
a) $1000^{\frac{1}{3}}$ b) $28^{\frac{1}{2}}$ c) $0.04^{\frac{1}{2}}$ d) $1.1^{\frac{1}{5}}$

5 Write these as combinations of roots and powers, then evaluate them. Give answers to 3 s.f. where necessary.
a) $16^{\frac{3}{4}}$ b) $125^{\frac{2}{3}}$ c) $5^{\frac{8}{8}}$ d) $100^{\frac{2}{5}}$
e) $8^{-\frac{1}{3}}$ f) $81^{-\frac{1}{4}}$ g) $729^{-\frac{2}{3}}$ h) $10^{-\frac{2}{5}}$

Check the facts

Round or approximate numbers when you don't want 'as much detail'. You can round to the nearest whole number, ten, hundred, thousand, etc. You can also round to a given number of decimal places (d.p.).

These tables show a number rounded in various ways. The **white** digits are the ones that have been rounded up or down.

Accurate number	to nearest thousand	to nearest hundred	to nearest ten	to nearest whole
1928.3746	2000	1900	1930	1928

Accurate number	to 1 d.p.	to 2 d.p.	to 3 d.p.
1928.3746	1928.4	1928.37	1928.375

You can also round to a given number of **significant figures** (s.f.).

Example: Round 35.71 to 3 s.f. The first three significant figures in the number are the 3, 5 and 7. The 7 represents 7 tenths. So you have to round to the nearest tenth (1 d.p.). 35.71 = 35.7 to 3 s.f.

Rounded numbers are often used for rough calculations called **estimations**. Normally, you round all the numbers to 1 s.f., then do the calculation in your head. This helps you check that an answer is the right size.

Test yourself

Complete the tables.

1

Accurate number	to nearest thousand	to nearest hundred	to nearest ten
6255			
15 640			
237			

2

Accurate number	to nearest whole	to 1 d.p.	to 2 d.p.	to 3 d.p.
1.6355				
0.004 56				
0.992				

3

Calculation	to 1 s.f.	to 2 s.f.	to 3 s.f.
18 ÷ 7			
$\sqrt{200}$			
1.25^5			

Check the facts

In science you often need to use very large or very small numbers.
Standard index form was invented to make it easier to write these down.

Powers of 10 are used to make the number roughly the right size.
Significant digits then make it exactly the right size.

For example, the number 2 million is
$2 \times 1\ 000\ 000 = 2 \times 10^6$.

$2\ 500\ 000$ is 2.5 million $= 2.5 \times 10^6$.

Numbers less than 1 need a **negative** index,
e.g. $0.002\ 13 = 2.13 \times 10^{-3}$.

> **Remember: a standard index form number consists of two
> parts: a number between 1 and 10 that contains the
> significant digits, and a power of 10.**

To enter a standard index form number into your calculator, look for a key
like one of these:

1.5×10^{13} could be displayed like one of these:

**Beware! Some older calculators use the last type of display. It looks
like 1.5^{13}, but doesn't mean that!**

Test yourself

1 Write in ordinary form:

   a) 2×10^4 b) 7×10^8 c) 1.5×10^6

   d) 5.66×10^9 e) 5×10^{-2} f) 8×10^{-7}

   g) 3.5×10^{-3} h) 4.75×10^{-1}

2 Write in standard index form:

   a) 3000   b) 40 000 000

   c) 650   d) 795 000

   e) 0.0006   f) 0.000 000 09

   g) 0.0095   h) 0.004 24

Check the facts

There are many different calculators available. For GCSE you need a scientific or graphic calculator.

All of these should apply the precedence order of operations (BoDMAS) automatically. However, if you are working out the answer to, say,

$$\frac{256}{3.35 + 4.65} \text{ and you type}$$

[2] [5] [6] [÷] [3] [.] [3] [5] [+] [4]

[.] [6] [5] [=] , you will get the wrong answer because

the calculator does the division first. There are two ways round it. The first is to use the bracket keys to force the calculator to do the addition first.

Type [2] [5] [6] [÷] [(] [3] [.] [3] [5] [+]
[4] [.] [6] [5] [)] [=] .

The second is to work out the addition separately, store it in the memory and recall it later.

Type [3] [.] [3] [5] [+] [4] [.] [6] [5] [=] [MIN]

to do the addition and store the answer in the memory.

Then type [2] [5] [6] [÷] [MR] [=] to finish the calculation.

Some calculators have more than one memory. Make sure you know how to store and recall numbers.

Test yourself

1 Work out the answer to each calculation. Use the bracket keys.

a) $(2.5 + 3.5) \times 32$

b) $0.03 \times (61.6 - 43.2)$

c) $1.01(8 + 2 - 0.005)$

d) $4.32 \div (1.67 + 2.83)$

e) $\dfrac{1.331}{1.3 - 0.09}$

f) $\dfrac{48\,000}{32 \times 125}$

g) $1.33 \times \{(1.4 \times 10^8) - (5.5 \times 10^7)\}$ h) $(5.5 \div 2.5)^3$

2 Use the memory to work these out.

a) $(4.42 + 3.3) \times (63 \div 55.5)$

b) $\dfrac{1.728}{0.2 + 1.24}$

c) $\dfrac{13.5 - 45.1}{10.3 - 2.4}$

d) $(1.3 + 0.41)^2$

e) $\sqrt{3.5 - 1.36}$

f) $[3.2 \times (2.5 - 1.25)]$

g) $\dfrac{(8.5 \times 10^9) + (3.6 \times 10^{10})}{(2.937 \times 10^7) \div (3.3 \times 10^5)}$

h) $16^{(3.48 + 0.77)}$

Numbers and calculations

BBC GCSE Check and Test: Maths

Check the facts

Most calculators have more functions than you will need at GCSE. However, there are some you need to use. Your keys may look slightly different to these.

Key	Function	Notes
CE	cancel error	If you're in the middle of a calculation and you make a mistake entering a number, don't waste time by starting again. Press this key and just enter the number again.
DEL INS	delete and insert	Usually found on graphic calculators. Use them to correct mistakes.
+/− −	change sign/ negative	Used for entering negative numbers.
x^2 x^3	square /cube	Much quicker than 'multiplying by itself' or using the power key, if you've got them.
$\sqrt{}$ $\sqrt[3]{}$	square root/ cube root	Do you press it before or after the number?
y^x $y^{\frac{1}{x}}$	power/root	Do you enter the base or index first?
exp	standard form	Don't type [2] [.] [3] [×] [1] [0] [exp] [6], type [2] [.] [3] [exp] [6]
π	pi	Make sure you know where this is. Use it in circle calculations.
DRG	angle mode	Make sure your calculator is set to degrees.
sin sin⁻¹	trig functions	Do you press them before or after number?
cos cos⁻¹	and inverse	If the angle mode is set wrongly, all these keys give the wrong answer!
tan tan⁻¹	trig functions	

Test yourself

Work out the value of each expression. Round answers to 3 d.p. where necessary.

1 a) $\sqrt{30}$ b) $\sqrt{0.008}$ c) $\sqrt[3]{125}$ d) $\sqrt[3]{1.1}$

2 a) $-2 \times 4^{1.5}$ b) $10^3 \div 2^{10}$ c) $\sqrt[4]{625}$ d) $\sqrt[6]{8}$

3 a) $(3 \times 10^6) + (6 \times 10^4)$ b) $(5.12 \times 10^4) \div (2.56 \times 10^2)$

c) $(9.95 \times 10^{-4}) \div (5 \times 10^{-6})$ d) $\sqrt{(4.9 \times 10^9)}$

4 a) $\pi + 1.5$ b) 5π c) $\dfrac{12}{\pi}$ d) $4^2 \times \pi$

h **5** a) $\cos 20°$ b) $3 \times \sin 40°$ c) $\dfrac{85}{\sin 85°}$

Check the facts

Fractions that contain different numbers may mean the same thing. These diagrams show some fractions that are equivalent to $\frac{2}{3}$.

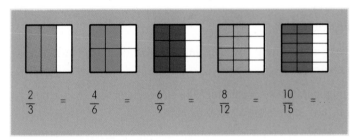

$$\frac{2}{3} = \frac{4}{6} = \frac{6}{9} = \frac{8}{12} = \frac{10}{15} = \ldots$$

To find equivalent fractions, multiply (or divide) the numerator and denominator by the same number:

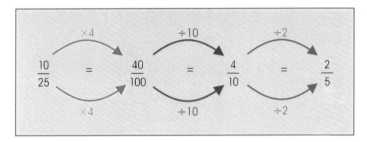

$$\frac{10}{25} \overset{\times 4}{\underset{\times 4}{=}} \frac{40}{100} \overset{\div 10}{\underset{\div 10}{=}} \frac{4}{10} \overset{\div 2}{\underset{\div 2}{=}} \frac{2}{5}$$

The last step produces the smallest whole numbers. The fraction $\frac{2}{5}$ is in its **lowest terms**. Finding lowest terms is called **simplifying** or **cancelling**.

Test yourself

1 Cancel each fraction to lowest terms.

a) $\frac{6}{8}$ b) $\frac{10}{20}$ c) $\frac{3}{9}$ d) $\frac{12}{15}$

e) $\frac{24}{27}$ f) $\frac{9}{12}$ g) $\frac{6}{10}$ h) $\frac{16}{20}$

i) $\frac{10}{16}$ j) $\frac{35}{100}$

2   Find the missing numbers.

a) $\frac{1}{6} = \frac{2}{?} = \frac{?}{30} = \frac{10}{?}$ b) $\frac{3}{8} = \frac{9}{?} = \frac{?}{32} = \frac{75}{?}$

c) $\frac{180}{200} = \frac{45}{?} = \frac{?}{40} = \frac{?}{10}$ d) $\frac{9}{?} = \frac{?}{200} = \frac{16}{64} = \frac{?}{4}$

Check the facts

Proper fractions have a smaller number on the top than on the bottom. **Improper fractions** don't fit this rule. They are sometimes called **top-heavy fractions**.

Examples: $\frac{5}{2}, \frac{8}{8}, \frac{101}{10}$.

Mixed fractions have a whole number part and a proper fraction.
Examples: $2\frac{3}{4}, 3\frac{1}{3}, 18\frac{25}{32}$.

An improper fraction usually matches a mixed fraction. For example, $2\frac{5}{8}$ means two whole ones and five eighths:

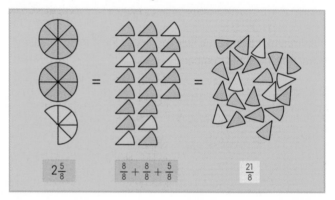

$$2\frac{5}{8} \qquad \frac{8}{8} + \frac{8}{8} + \frac{5}{8} \qquad \frac{21}{8}$$

Rules

To change a mixed fraction $W\frac{n}{d}$ **to an improper fraction:**

- Multiply W by d and add n. This is the numerator.
- Use d as the denominator. The improper fraction is $\frac{Wd+n}{d}$.

To change an improper fraction $\frac{N}{d}$ **to a mixed fraction:**

- Divide N by d. The 'answer' gives the whole number part w. The remainder r is the numerator for the fraction part.
- Use d as the denominator. The mixed fraction is $w\frac{r}{d}$.

Test yourself

1 Write as improper fractions: a) $1\frac{1}{2}$ b) $2\frac{1}{4}$ c) $3\frac{1}{3}$ d) $5\frac{5}{8}$ e) $2\frac{7}{10}$ f) $1\frac{17}{24}$

2 Write as mixed fractions: a) $\frac{7}{2}$ b) $\frac{7}{3}$ c) $\frac{11}{5}$ d) $\frac{11}{8}$ e) $\frac{37}{20}$ f) $\frac{583}{100}$

3 Are these statements true or false? a) $6\frac{1}{4} = \frac{25}{4}$ b) $1\frac{11}{16} = \frac{25}{16}$ c) $\frac{14}{3} = 4\frac{2}{3}$
   d) $\frac{15}{8} = 1\frac{5}{8}$ e) $8\frac{4}{9} = \frac{74}{9}$ f) $\frac{38}{12} = 3\frac{1}{6}$

Check the facts

You can only add or subtract fractions if they have the same denominator. If you want to add or subtract fractions with different denominators, you have to change some of them to equivalent fractions so that the bottom numbers match.

Examples:

- $\frac{3}{7} + \frac{1}{7} = \frac{4}{7}$

- $\frac{1}{2} - \frac{1}{6}$

  You can't write an equivalent fraction for $\frac{1}{6}$ as halves, but you can write $\frac{1}{2}$ as $\frac{3}{6}$.

  So $\frac{1}{2} - \frac{1}{6} = \frac{3}{6} - \frac{1}{6} = \frac{2}{6} = \frac{1}{3}$.

- $\frac{5}{6} + \frac{3}{4}$:

  You can't match either of the denominators. You have to multiply them both to find a **common denominator**. You could use $6 \times 4 = 24$, but 12 is better.

  So $\frac{5}{6} + \frac{3}{4} = \frac{10}{12} + \frac{9}{12} = \frac{19}{12} = 1\frac{7}{12}$

- Subtracting a proper fraction from 1 is always easy.

  $1 - \frac{1}{10} = \frac{9}{10}$, $1 - \frac{2}{5} = \frac{3}{5}$, $1 - \frac{21}{25} = \frac{4}{25}$, etc.

Test yourself

Give answers in lowest terms. Convert answers to mixed fractions if necessary.

1 Add these fractions.

  a) $\frac{1}{9} + \frac{4}{9}$ b) $\frac{3}{10} + \frac{1}{10}$ c) $\frac{5}{8} + \frac{1}{4}$ d) $\frac{5}{6} + \frac{3}{8}$ e) $\frac{1}{12} + \frac{1}{8} + \frac{1}{10}$

2 Subtract these.

  a) $\frac{3}{4} - \frac{5}{16}$ b) $\frac{7}{10} - \frac{1}{5}$ c) $\frac{8}{9} - \frac{1}{6}$ d) $\frac{5}{14} - \frac{2}{21}$ e) $\frac{4}{15} + \frac{1}{5} - \frac{3}{10}$

3 Convert the mixed fractions to improper fractions before you start.

  a) $1\frac{3}{5} + \frac{7}{10}$ b) $1\frac{2}{3} - \frac{1}{4}$ c) $6\frac{5}{8} - 2\frac{1}{2}$ d) $4\frac{9}{10} + 3\frac{1}{3}$ e) $2\frac{1}{10} - 1\frac{3}{8} + \frac{11}{20}$

4 What is:

  a) $1 - \frac{1}{4}$ b) $1 - \frac{1}{12}$ c) $1 - \frac{4}{9}$ d) $1 - \frac{7}{10}$ e) $1 - \frac{99}{100}$

Fractions and percentages

BBC GCSE Check and Test: Maths

Fractions and percentages

Check the facts

To multiply two fractions together, just multiply the top and bottom numbers separately.

$$\frac{3}{4} \times \frac{7}{10} = \frac{3 \times 7}{4 \times 10} = \frac{21}{40}$$

You can always get the answer like this, but sometimes it can lead to a lot of cancelling.

$$\frac{5}{8} \times \frac{16}{25} = \frac{5 \times 16}{8 \times 25} = \frac{80}{200} .\text{ This cancels to } \frac{2}{5} \text{ !}$$

It can be easier to **cross-cancel**. This means doing some of the cancelling **before** you multiply.

$$\frac{5}{8} \times \frac{16}{25} = \frac{1}{8} \times \frac{16}{5} \quad \textit{(Cancelled 5 and 25 to 1 and 5.)}$$
$$\frac{1}{8} \times \frac{16}{5} = \frac{1}{1} \times \frac{2}{5} \quad \textit{(Cancelled 8 and 16 to 1 and 2.)}$$

This is obviously $\frac{2}{5}$. You are less likely to make a mistake this way because the numbers involved in the working are smaller.

Mixed fractions **must** be converted to improper ones first.

To divide two fractions, invert the second one (turn it upside down) and turn the ÷ into a ×.

$$2\frac{1}{4} \div \frac{3}{8} = \frac{9}{4} \div \frac{3}{8} \quad \textit{(Made mixed fraction improper.)}$$
$$\frac{9}{4} \div \frac{3}{8} = \frac{9}{4} \times \frac{8}{3} \quad \textit{(Inverted second fraction.)}$$
$$\frac{9}{4} \times \frac{8}{3} = \frac{3}{1} \times \frac{2}{1} \quad \textit{(Cross-cancelled.)}$$
$$\frac{3}{1} \times \frac{2}{1} = \frac{6}{1} = 6$$

Test yourself

1 Multiply:

a) $\frac{1}{4} \times \frac{3}{5}$ b) $\frac{2}{5} \times \frac{4}{9}$ c) $\frac{7}{10} \times \frac{5}{8}$ d) $\frac{5}{12} \times \frac{8}{15}$

e) $1\frac{1}{3} \times \frac{1}{3}$ f) $2\frac{1}{4} \times \frac{2}{3}$ g) $3\frac{1}{3} \times 1\frac{1}{2}$ h) $\frac{7}{10} \times 4\frac{2}{7}$

2 Divide:

a) $\frac{1}{4} \div \frac{1}{16}$ b) $\frac{2}{5} \div \frac{1}{10}$ c) $3\frac{1}{3} \div \frac{5}{6}$ d) $2\frac{3}{4} \div \frac{11}{12}$

e) $5\frac{2}{5} \div 1\frac{4}{5}$ f) $10\frac{1}{2} \div 1\frac{3}{4}$ g) $\frac{4}{9} \div 2\frac{2}{3}$ h) $\frac{11}{20} \div 3\frac{1}{7}$

Check the facts

> To find $\frac{1}{4}$ of something, divide by 4.
>
> To find $\frac{1}{5}$ of something, divide by 5, and so on.
>
> **This method works for unit fractions.**

To find other fractions, first work out the unit fraction, then multiply by the numerator.

> *Example*: Find $\frac{7}{10}$ of £150.
>
> $\frac{1}{10}$ of £150 = £150 ÷ 10 = 15
>
> $\frac{7}{10}$ of £150 = 7 × £15 = £105

If you have a fraction of something and you want to work out the original amount, just work backwards.

> *Example*: $\frac{2}{5}$ of a cake weighs 240 g.
>
> So $\frac{1}{5}$ weighs 240 ÷ 2 = 120 g.
>
> So the whole cake weighed 120 × 5 = 600 g.

Test yourself

1 Find these unit fractions:

a) $\frac{1}{2}$ of £50   b) $\frac{1}{5}$ of 200 g   c) $\frac{1}{10}$ of 35 km

d) $\frac{1}{6}$ of 72 cl   e) $\frac{1}{8}$ of 100 m^2

2 Find these fractions:

a) $\frac{3}{4}$ of £180   b) $\frac{2}{3}$ of 198 kg   c) $\frac{5}{8}$ of 5 litres

d) $\frac{9}{10}$ of 2 million people   e) $\frac{5}{12}$ of 108 ohms

f) $\frac{33}{100}$ of £95   g) $\frac{5}{6}$ of 300 m   h) $\frac{2}{5}$ of 8000 votes

i) $\frac{3}{16}$ of 2.5 cm   j) $\frac{19}{20}$ of 50 tonnes

3 Find the original amounts:

a) $\frac{3}{10}$ is £30   b) $\frac{4}{5}$ is 128 days   c) $\frac{9}{20}$ is 45 km

d) $\frac{3}{8}$ is 4 hours   e) $\frac{6}{100}$ is 12 cm^3

BBC GCSE Check and Test: Maths

Check the facts

Remember that a percentage is just a fraction with a denominator of 100.
So $35\% = \frac{35}{100} = 0.35$, $7\% = \frac{7}{100} = 0.07$.

To convert a fraction to a percentage, you have to 'steer' the denominator towards 100.

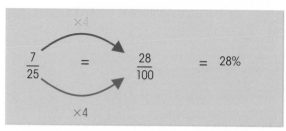

$$\frac{7}{25} = \frac{28}{100} = 28\%$$

×4

×4

Sometimes you can't do this straight away. You have to go above 100 first.

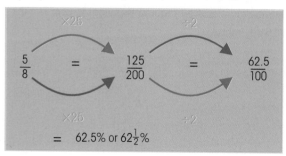

$$\frac{5}{8} = \frac{125}{200} = \frac{62.5}{100}$$

×25   ÷2

×25   ÷2

$$= 62.5\% \text{ or } 62\tfrac{1}{2}\%$$

Another way is to turn the fraction into a decimal first.

$\frac{7}{25} = 7 \div 25 = 0.28 = 28\%$.

$\frac{5}{8} = 5 \div 8 = 0.625 = 62.5\%$.

Test yourself

1 Complete the table. Each line represents one fraction.

	Frac	Dec	%			Frac	Dec	%
a)	$\frac{1}{2}$			g)		$\frac{1}{8}$		
b)		0.25		h)				17.5%
c)	$\frac{1}{10}$			i)		$\frac{31}{50}$		
d)			20%	j)			1	
e)		0.6		k)		$\frac{1}{3}$		
f)		0.65		l)		$\frac{2}{3}$		

2 Change each set to the same form, then write them in order of size, smallest to biggest.

a) 26%, $\frac{1}{4}$, 22%, 0.235, $\frac{6}{25}$, 0.3   b) $\frac{2}{3}$, 66%, 0.67, $\frac{27}{40}$, $\frac{5}{8}$, 0.666

Fractions and percentages

Check the facts

There are two main ways to work out a percentage of something.

1 Divide the amount by 100 to find 1%, then multiply by the number of per cent.

Example: Find 35% of £40.

$$1\% = £40 \div 100 = £0.40.$$
$$35\% = £0.40 \times 35 = £14.$$

2 Convert the percentage to a decimal, then multiply the amount by this.

Example: Find 35% of £40.

$$35\% = 0.35.$$
$$£40 \times 0.35 = £14.$$

If you know a percentage of an amount and want to know what the original amount was, reverse the two methods.

1 Divide by the number of per cent to find 1%, then multiply by 100.

Example: 35% of a race is 105 km.

How far is the full distance?

1% of the race = 105 km ÷ 35 = 3 km.

100% of the race = 3 km × 100 = 300 km.

2 Convert the percentage to a decimal, then divide the amount by this.

Example: 35% of a race is 105 km. How far is the full distance?

$$35\% = 0.35.$$
$$105 \text{ km} \div 0.35 = 300 \text{ km}.$$

Test yourself

1 Work out these percentages. Use the first method.
   a) 5% of £2500
   b) 60% of 90 kg
   c) 45% of 10 km^2
   d) 1% of 600 000 people
   e) 17.5% of £6.99
   f) 130% of 4000 litres

2 Work out these percentages. Use the second method.
   a) 10% of £2500
   b) 88% of 24 hours
   c) 25% of 500 cm^3
   d) 2.5% of £150
   e) 0.5% of 300 volts
   f) 220% of 55 kg

3 What was the original amount in each case? Use the method you prefer.
   a) 20% is 800 m
   b) 35% is 7 tonnes
   c) 60% is 1.5 mm
   d) 4% is 75 km/h
   e) 12.5% is 450 Mb
   f) 99% is 5000 years

Check the facts

> **A percentage increase is a percentage added on to an amount. Work out the increase and add it on.**

Example: What is 40 kg increased by 20%?

20% of 40 kg = 8 kg

40 kg + 8 kg = 48 kg.

> **Percentage decreases work the same way. Work out the decrease and subtract it.**

Example: John's car cost £9000 new. Its value has decreased by 15%.

What is it worth now?

15% of £9000 = £1350

£9000 − £1350 = £7650.

Test yourself

1 Everyone at a factory gets a 5% pay rise. Work out what they earn after the rise.

Julie	Malcolm	Serena	James	Mitchell
£15 500	£12 850	£8000	£19 655	£4500

2 Jasmin bought a new car a long time ago. This table shows how much of its value it had lost after various numbers of years.

New	1 year old	2 year old	5 years old	10 years old
£12 500	12%	17%	32%	65%

How much was the car worth at each stage?

3 In these questions you are given the starting figure, then the new figure after a percentage change.

In each case, work out whether there has been an increase or decrease, and what the percentage is.

a) £12 → £15

b) 40 m → 42 m

c) 200 g → 160 g

d) £7500 → £6375

e) 30 000 → 31 200

f) 50% → 45%

Check the facts

A reverse change is one where you know the amount after
a percentage change and want to find the original amount.
The safest way to do this is to use the decimal method.

Example: Madhur got a 10% pay rise, bringing her wages to
£198 per week. What did she earn before the rise?

Madhur is now earning 100% + 10% = 110% of her old wages. That
means her wages were multiplied by 1.1. To reverse this, divide by 1.1.

£198 ÷ 1.1 = £180.

Example: The water level in a reservoir fell by 6% to 14.1 m. What was
the level before?

The level is now 100% − 6% = 94% of what it was before, so the original
level has been multiplied by 0.94. To reverse this, divide by 0.94.

14.1 m ÷ 0.94 = 15 m.

Test yourself

Work out the amounts before the percentage changes. Complete the table.

	Percentage change	Final amount	Original amount
1	10% increase	121 hectares	
2	35% increase	£16 200	
3	5% decrease	37.05 m	
4	16% increase	29 years	
5	1% increase	12 322 cm^3	
6	50% decrease	68 staff	
7	$12\frac{1}{2}$% increase	0.729 m^2	
8	0.6% decrease	5467 litres	
9	110% increase	44.1 kb	
10	99% decrease	13 seconds	

Fractions and percentages

BBC GCSE Check and Test: Maths

23

Check the facts

Suppose two amounts behave like this:

• one amount is always a fixed multiple of the other

• whenever one amount is multiplied or divided by something, so is the other

then the amounts are said to be **in direct proportion**, or **directly proportional to each other**.

If y is directly proportional to x, this is written $y \propto x$. That means $y = kx$, where k is the **constant of proportionality**.

Example: if 10 litres of petrol cost £7, 20 litres will cost double, £14, and 5 litres will cost half, £3.50. The number of litres is multiplied by 0.7 to get the cost.

Let C be the cost and L be the number of litres. Then $C \propto L$. The formula is $C = 0.7L$.

If you plot two proportional amounts against each other on a graph, you get a straight line through the origin.

Test yourself

Round answers appropriately where necessary.

1 A shop sells writing paper at 40 sheets for £1.
  a) How much will 100 sheets cost?
  b) How many sheets could you buy for 70p?

2 25 cm^3 of silver weighs 262.5 grams.
  a) An ingot is 15 cm × 4 cm × 6 cm. How much does it weigh?
  b) Janine's necklace weighs 42 grams. What volume of silver was used to make it? *(Hint: find the volume of 1 gram.)*

3 Javed buys 4.5 kg of potatoes for £1.35.
  a) How much will 2.5 kg cost?
  b) What weight of potatoes could you buy for £2?

4 One gallon is 4.54 litres.
  a) Change 3.5 gallons into litres.
  b) Convert 10 litres to gallons.

5 One euro is worth £0.61.
  a) How many £ are worth 5.50 euros?
  b) How many euros is £1 worth?
  c) Draw a conversion graph for £ and euros, for up to 10 euros.

Check the facts

Any amounts that are in direct proportion are also in a constant ratio
For example, suppose 10 pens cost £4. Then the ratio can be written:

number : cost = 10 : 4. Say 'to' when you see a colon (:).

Ratios can be equivalent to each other, just like fractions.
So 10 : 4 = 20 : 8 = 100 : 40.

Ratios can be cancelled to **lowest terms**. 10 : 4 = **5 : 2** in lowest terms. It contains the smallest whole numbers possible.

Sometimes it's useful to write a ratio in **unitary** form. That means one of the numbers is a 1.

Dividing both sides by 10, 10 : 4 = 1 : 0.4. A pen costs £0.40.
Cost = 0.4 × number, $C = 0.4n$.

Dividing both sides by 4, 10 : 4 = **2.5 : 1**. You get 2.5 pens for £1.
Number = 2.5 × cost, $n = 2.5C$.

Test yourself

1 Write these ratios
   i) in lowest terms
   ii) in unitary form, with 1 on the left
   iii) in unitary form, with 1 on the right

   a) 2 : 10   b) 12 : 3   c) 15 : 18
   d) 20 : 25   e) 100 : 45

2 A map is on a scale of 1 : 25 000.
   a) What do these measurements on the map mean in reality?
      i) 1 cm   ii) 10 cm   iii) 12.8 cm

   b) How are these distances represented on the map?
      i) 1 km   ii) 15 km   iii) 100 km

3 On a car journey, the ratio of time taken to distance travelled is 30 minutes : 40 km.
   a) What distance is travelled in 10 minutes?
   b) What distance is travelled in 1 minute?
   c) How long does it take to travel 25 km?
   d) What is the speed of the car in km/h?

4 Write proportion formulae using answers (ii) and (iii) from each part of question 1. Use any letters you like.

Fractions and percentages

BBC GCSE Check and Test: Maths

Check the facts

Sometimes you need to divide amounts in a certain ratio.

Example: Phoebe wants to divide £1000 between her grandchildren in the ratio of their ages. Freddie is 6 and Lucy is 4. How much does each receive?

The ratio is Freddie : Lucy = 6 : 4. There are a total of 10 'shares', so one 'share' is £100.

So Freddie gets 6 shares = £600 and Lucy gets 4 shares = £400.

A big difference between fractions and ratios is that ratios can have more than two parts.

Example: In a spice mix, the ratio of coriander : cumin : paprika = 4 : 3 : 1. Stefan used 36 g of coriander. How much did he make altogether, and how much of the other ingredients did he use?

Paprika: 4 'shares' in the mix = 36 g, so 1 'share' = 9 g.

Cumin: 3 'shares' = 27 g.

Whole mix: 8 'shares' altogether = 72 g.

Test yourself

Complete the table.

	Amount	Ratio (lowest terms)	Shares
1	£500	2 : 3	? : ?
2	160 kg	3 : 5	? : ?
3	?	6 : 3 : 1	? : ? : 8 ml
4	?	? : ?	19.6 cm : 14.7 cm
5	1331 sec	1 : 10	? : ?
6	£1000	2 : 3 : 5	? : ? : ?
7	60 km	5 : ? : 3	25 km : ? : ?
8	?	? : ? : ?	0.2 g : 1.2 g : 1.4 g
9	350 t	2 : 5 : 3 : 4	? : ? : ? : ?
10	640 l	? : 5 : 1	400 l : ? : ?

Check the facts

In a scale drawing or model, or on a map, all the 'real' measurements are multiplied or divided by the **scale factor** of the drawing. This is different to a sketch diagram, where the lengths don't have to be right as long as the measurements are marked.

A 1 : 40 scale model of a boat is $\frac{1}{40}$ of the actual size of the boat.

A map drawn on a scale of 1 : 50 000 is $\frac{1}{50\,000}$ of the actual size of the area it covers.

A diagram of a circuit on a scale of 25 : 1 is 25 times larger than the real thing.

Test yourself

1 This plan of a house and garden is drawn on a scale of 1 : 400.

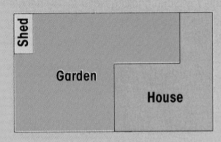

a) Draw a copy of the plan. Mark on the actual measurements.
b) What actual area is covered by: i) the whole plot? ii) the house?
   iii) the shed? iv) the garden?

2 This is a sketch diagram of a logo to be printed on a computer chip.

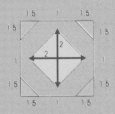

All measurements are in mm. Make an accurate drawing, on a scale of 20 : 1.

3 The length of a model plane is 32 cm. The actual length of the real plane is 16 m. The wingspan of the model is 25 cm.
a) What is the scale of the model?
b) What is the actual wingspan of the plane?

Check the facts

Inverse proportion is another type of relationship between amounts. You usually find it where there's a fixed amount of something to be divided up.

Suppose two amounts behave like this:

- one amount times the other is a fixed number
- whenever one amount is multiplied by something, the other is divided

then the amounts are said to be in **inverse proportion**, or **inversely proportional to each other**.

If y is inversely proportional to x, this is written $y \propto \dfrac{1}{x}$.

h

That means $y = \dfrac{k}{x}$ or $xy = k$, where k is the **constant of proportionality**.

> *Example*: If there's enough drinking water for 30 people to have 10 litres each, then 60 people could only have 5 litres each, half as much, and 15 people could have 20 litres each, twice as much.
>
> Let w be the number of litres and p be the number of people. Then $w \propto \dfrac{1}{p}$. The formula is $w = \dfrac{300}{p}$ or
>
> $wp = 300$. $k = 300$, the total amount of water available.

Test yourself

1 A fixed sum of money is to be divided between a number of people. If everyone gets £50, there is enough for 150 people.
   a) How much money is available?
   b) How much would everyone get if there were 120 people?
   c) How many people could be given £37.50 each?

2 The current in an electrical circuit is inversely proportional to the resistance. When the resistance is 3000 Ω (ohms), the current is 2 A (amps).

h

   a) What will the current be when the resistance is
      i) 1500 Ω   ii) 5000 Ω?

   b) What will the resistance be when the current is
      i) 2.5 A   ii) 0.5 A?

   c) The constant of proportionality is the voltage in the circuit. What is it?

Check the facts

Substitution is replacing letters in a formula, equation or expression by numbers called their **values**.

When you do this, you need to be careful to **evaluate** parts of the formula in the correct order, using BoDMAS (page 6).

> Suppose that $a = 2$, $x = 10$ and $y = 5$.
>
> Then $3x + 4 = 3 \times 10 + 4 = 30 + 4 = 34$,
> but $3(x + 4) = 3 \times (10 + 4) = 3 \times 14 = 42$.
>
> Also $ay^2 = 2 \times 5^2 = 2 \times 25 = 50$,
> but $(ay)^2 = (2 \times 5)^2 = 10^2 = 100$.

Test yourself

1 If $p = 10$ and $q = 2.5$, evaluate

a) $p + q$ b) $2p + q$ c) $q - p$

d) pq e) $\frac{p}{q}$ f) $\frac{q}{p}$

g) $\frac{p-q}{p}$ h) $2(p + q)$ i) p^2

j) $\sqrt{\frac{p}{q}}$

2 $s = ut + \frac{1}{2}at^2$. Find s when

a) $u = 0$, $a = 10$, $t = 5$.

b) $u = 10$, $a = 0$, $t = 5$.

c) $u = 10$, $a = 5$, $t = 10$.

d) $u = -10$, $a = 5$, $t = 5$.

e) $u = 0.1$, $a = 0.01$, $t = 1000$.

3 If $A = 45°$, $B = 60°$, $C = 90°$ and $x = 0.5$, evaluate:

a) $\sin A$ b) $\tan B$

c) $\cos C$ d) $\sin^{-1} x$

e) $\cos^{-1} x$ f) $\tan^{-1} x$

g) $\sin (A + B)$ h) $\tan (C - A)$

Algebra

BBC GCSE Check and Test: Maths

Check the facts

Expressions in algebra are made up of a number of terms added or subtracted together.

$2a + 3b - \frac{c}{4}$ is an expression with three terms.

Each term is made up of letters and numbers multiplied or divided together.

Sometimes you find the same kind of term more than once in an expression. These are called **like terms**. You can combine these to simplify the expression.

Example: Simplify $2p + 3q + 4p - 7q$.

- You can rearrange the terms as long as you keep their signs with them.

$2p + 3q + 4p - 7q = 2p + 4p + 3q - 7q$ *(Rearrange the terms.)*

$= 6p - 4q$.   *(Combine 'p' terms and 'q' terms.)*

- You don't *have* to rearrange the terms. You can combine terms straight away if you can see the answer.

Note:

uv and vu are like terms because the order in which you multiply doesn't matter.

$\frac{x}{2}$ and $\frac{2}{x}$ are *not* like terms, because the order of division *does* matter.

Also $3n$ and $3n^2$ are *not* like terms, because $3n^2$ has more n's multiplied together.

Test yourself

Simplify each expression as much as possible.

1   $3a + 4a + 5a$ 2 $2r + 6r - 5r$

3   $s + 4s - 2t$ 4 $2y + 5z + 3y + z$

5   $10h + 4k - 3h - 8k$ 6 $4x + 5 - 6x - 2$

7   $3n^2 + 2n + n^2 + n$ 8 $4x^2 + 2x + 2x + 1$

9   $\frac{1}{u} + \frac{2}{u}$ 10 $\frac{c}{4} + \frac{c}{4}$

Check the facts

> When multiplying two terms together:
> - multiply the numbers first
> - multiply the letters in turn (see Index Rules, page 9).

Example: $2ab^2 \times 4a^3c = 8a^4b^2c$,

because $2 \times 4 = 8$, $a \times a^3 = a^4$,

there are no b's in the second term,

there are no c's in the first term.

When dividing terms:

- Write the question in fraction style if it's not already written that way.
- Cancel the numbers as if you were cancelling a fraction to lowest terms.
- Divide the letters in turn. Each letter remains on the top or bottom depending on where the larger power occurs.

Example: $2x^3yz^2 \div 10xyz^4 = \dfrac{2x^3yz^2}{10xyz^4} = \dfrac{x^2}{5z^2}$,

because $\frac{2}{10}$ cancels to $\frac{1}{5}$, and when there are letters present,

you don't write '1', x^3 and x cancel to x^2 on the top, the y's cancel each other out completely, z^2 and z^4 cancel to z^2 on the bottom.

Test yourself

1 Multiply:

   a) $4a \times 3b$ b) $2t \times t^2$ c) $f \times 5fg$

   d) $2n^2m \times 3nm$ e) $4uv^5 \times 6u^2v^2$ f) $8i \times 4j^2 \times 2ij$

2 Divide:

   a) $\dfrac{4x^3}{x}$ b) $\dfrac{3ab^2}{6ab}$ c) $\dfrac{10rs}{4rt}$

   d) $2n^2m \div 5nm^2$ e) $24xyz \div 8x^2y^2z^2$ f) $10c^8d^5 \div 12c^4d^{12}$

3 These have multiplication and division combined.

   a) $\dfrac{3p^2qr \times 4pqr}{6p^3qr^3}$

   b) $\dfrac{5c^2t}{ct^3 \times c^3}$

   c) $\dfrac{10a \times 2a^2}{5a \times a^2}$

Algebra

BBC GCSE Check and Test: Maths

Algebra

Check the facts

> When a number multiplies a bracket, everything inside the bracket is multiplied.

So $3(100 - 10) = 3 \times 100 - 3 \times 10 = 300 - 30 = 270$.

The same principle applies in algebra.

So $2(x + y) = 2x + 2y$.
The process of removing the brackets like this is called **expansion**.

This also works with division.

So $\dfrac{(a+b)}{2} = \dfrac{a}{2} + \dfrac{b}{2}$ or $\dfrac{1}{2}(a+b) = \dfrac{a}{2} + \dfrac{b}{2}$.

You can multiply a bracket by a letter or expression.

So $a(x + y) = ax + ay$ and $ak^2(ak + 1) = a^2k^3 + ak^2$.

Test yourself

1 Expand these expressions:

a) $2(a + b)$ b) $3(a - b)$ c) $4(2a + b)$

d) $10(3a + 5b)$ e) $-2(a + 2b)$ f) $5(-a + b)$

2 Expand:

a) $u(u + v)$ b) $u(2u - v)$ c) $v(3u - 4v)$

d) $2u(u + v)$ e) $5u(2u + 3v)$ f) $-v(u + v)$

3 Expand:

a) $xy(x + y)$ b) $2xy(4x + 6y)$ c) $-3xy(2x - y)$

d) $10xy(y - x)$ e) $xy(y^2 - x^2)$ f) $4x^2y(2xy - xy^2)$

4 Expand, then simplify:

a) $2(p + q) + 3(p + 2q)$ b) $3(p + q) + 2(4p - 2q)$

c) $2(3p - q) + 4(2p + 2q)$ d) $p(p + q) + q(p + 2q)$

e) $2p(2p - q) + 3q(6p + 2q)$ f) $3q(p - 5q) - p(10p + 3q)$

Check the facts

Factorising is the opposite of expansion. To factorise, you look for common factors between the terms.

For example, in the expression $2x + 2y$, each term is $2 \times$ a letter, so 2 is the common factor.

So $2x + 2y = 2(x + y)$.

This process is called **extracting factors**. Sometimes you need to do this in more than one step.

$$6ab^2 - 4a^2b = 2(3ab^2 - 2a^2b) \quad \text{(Extracted 2.)}$$
$$= 2a(3b^2 - 2ab) \quad \text{(Extracted a.)}$$
$$= 2ab(3b - 2a) \quad \text{(Extracted b – finished.)}$$

Test yourself

Factorise these expressions as fully as possible.

1 a) $4e + 4f$

b) $7e - 21f$

c) $-5e + 5f$

d) $-4e - 6f$

2 a) $w^2 + wz$

b) $3w^2 - wz$

c) $4w^2 + 3wz$

d) $wz + 2z^2$

3 a) $3A^2 + 3AB$

b) $12A^2 + 28AB$

c) $AB - 6B^2$

d) $-6A^2 - 3AB$

4 a) $p^2t + pt^2$

b) $4p^2t - 8pt^2$

c) $6p^2t + 15pt^2$

d) $-20p^2t + 10pt^2$

Algebra

BBC GCSE Check and Test: Maths

Check the facts

When you have to expand an expression like $(a + b)(x + y)$, **everything** in the first bracket has to be multiplied by **everything** in the second bracket. The difficult thing is making sure you don't miss a term! Use *F-O-I-L* to help you.

$(a + b)(x + y)$	ax	First term in both brackets
$(a + b)(x + y)$	ay	Outer terms
$(a + b)(x + y)$	bx	Inner terms
$(a + b)(x + y)$	by	Last term in both brackets

So $(a + b)(x + y) = ax + ay + bx + by$.

Be careful with signs. For example,

$(e - 3)(e - 2) = e^2 - 2e - 3e + 6$ *(F-O-I-L)*

$\qquad\qquad\quad = e^2 - 5e + 6$ *(Combine 'e' terms.)*

Test yourself

1 Expand these expressions.

  a) $(a + b)(x - y)$

  b) $(a - b)(x + y)$

  c) $(a - b)(x - y)$

  d) $(2a + b)(2c + d)$

  e) $(2a - 3b)(c + 4d)$

  f) $(5i + 3j)(2k - 2l)$

2 Expand and simplify:

  a) $(x + 1)(x + 4)$

  b) $(x + 3)(x - 2)$

  c) $(x - 8)(x + 2)$

  d) $(p + 5)(p - 1)$

  e) $(a + b)(a - b)$

  f) $(a + b)^2$

Algebra

www.bbc.co.uk/revision

Check the facts

> **A quadratic expression has a letter-squared term, possibly a letter term and a number.**

Examples: $3x^2 + 4x + 1$, $p^2 - p$, $10x^2 + 6$.

Quadratic expressions can sometimes be factorised into two brackets. To do this, use the **FOIL** rule in reverse (see page 34).

Example: Factorise $6x^2 + 7x - 20$.

First write down a list of the numbers that could be part of the **FIRST** pair. Write down a list of the numbers that could be part of the **LAST** pair. Organise them in a table like this:

	first in bracket (x)				last in bracket (number)					
1st bracket	1	2	3	6	1	2	4	5	10	20
2nd bracket	6	3	2	1	-20	-10	-5	-4	-2	-1

Test combinations of these numbers to see if you can make the **INNER** and **OUTER** pairs match the letter term in the expression you want to factorise. In this diagram, the combination being tested is $(x + 4)(6x - 5)$.

	first in bracket (x)				last in bracket (number)					
1st bracket	1	2	3	6	1	2	4	5	10	20
2nd bracket	6	3	2	1	-20	-10	-5	-4	-2	-1

This one doesn't work, because $1 \times -5 = -5$ and $6 \times 4 = 24$. Together these make 19, which would be $19x$ in the expansion. This is the combination that makes $7x$:

	first in bracket (x)				last in bracket (number)					
1st bracket	1	2	3	6	1	2	4	5	10	20
2nd bracket	6	3	2	1	-20	-10	-5	-4	-2	-1

So $6x^2 + 7x - 20 = (2x + 5)(3x - 4)$.

A special case of this is called the **difference of two squares**

Example: Factorise $9p^2 - 25$.

$9p^2 - 25 = (3p)^2 - 5^2$, the difference of two squares.
$9p^2 - 25 = (3p + 5)(3p - 5)$.

Test yourself

Factorise these expressions:

1 $x^2 + 5x + 6$ **2** $x^2 + 5x - 6$ **3** $a^2 - a - 12$

4 $3x^2 + 10x - 8$ **5** $6x^2 + 7x - 20$ **6** $4p^2 - 24p + 32$

7 $x^2 - 16$ **8** $4x^2 - 100$ **9** $36N^2 - 1$

Check the facts

An equation is a puzzle that needs to be solved. The letter in the equation stands for a definite unknown number you have to find.

Example: Solve the equation $2x - 5 = 12$.

Think what you would have to do if you were substituting a number into the equation. $x \rightarrow$ multiply by 2 $\rightarrow$ subtract 5.

To find the answer, do the opposite things in the opposite order: add 5 $\rightarrow$ divide by 2.

$$2x - 5 = 12 \qquad \text{(Always write out the equation first.)}$$
$$2x = 12 + 5 \qquad \text{(First step: add 5 to both sides.)}$$
$$2x = 17 \qquad \text{(Simplify the right-hand side.)}$$
$$x = 17 \div 2 \qquad \text{(Second step: divide both sides by 2.)}$$
$$x = 8.5 \qquad \text{(Simplify the right-hand side. Finished.)}$$

The **solution** of the equation is $x = 8.5$. $x = 8.5$ **satisfies** the equation.

This method works with any mathematical operations.

Example: Solve the equation $3\sqrt{(x+1)} = 15$.

$$x \rightarrow \text{add 1} \rightarrow \text{square root} \rightarrow \text{multiply by 3.}$$

To 'unravel' these, divide by 3 $\rightarrow$ square $\rightarrow$ subtract 1.

$3\sqrt{(x+1)} = 15$. *(Always write out the equation first.)*

$\sqrt{(x+1)} = 15 \div 3 = 5$ *(First step: divide both sides by 3 and simplify.)*

$x + 1 = 5^2 = 25$ *(Second step: square both sides and simplify.)*

$x = 25 - 1 = 24$ *(Third step: subtract 1 from both sides and simplify.)*

Remember: An equation with a squared letter has two possible solutions.

Example: $x^2 = 4$ The solutions are $x = 2$ or
$x = -2$ since $2^2 = 4$ and $(-2)^2 = 4$

Test yourself

Solve each equation.

1 $x - 12 = 8$ **2** $5d = -20$ **3** $2w = \frac{1}{2}$

4 $3B + 2 = 11$ **5** $4f - 2 = 30$ **6** $2a - 6 = -10$

7 $12 - 4j = 8$ **8** $y^2 + 10 = 46$ **9** $3 + \sqrt{x} = 5$

10 $4x^2 = 100$ **11** $(n + 1)^2 = 16$ **12** $\sqrt{x - 8} = 9$

Algebra

www.bbc.co.uk/revision

Check the facts

There are two main situations in which you need to rearrange an equation before you can solve it.

1 The unknown letter occurs on both sides of the equation.

Example: $4x + 14 = 2 - 2x$	*(Write the equation first.)*
$4x + 2x + 14 = 2$	*(Add 2x to both sides.)*
$6x + 14 = 2$	*(Simplify.)*
$6x = 2 - 14$	*(Subtract 14 from both sides.)*
$6x = -12$	*(Simplify.)*
$x = -2$	*(Divide both sides by 6.)*

2 There is a bracket that has to be expanded.

Example: $2(3x - 5) = 8$	*(Write the equation first.)*
$6x - 10 = 8$	*(Expand the bracket.)*
$6x = 8 + 10$	*(Add 10 to both sides.)*
$6x = 18$	*(Simplify.)*
$x = 3$	*(Divide both sides by 6.)*

You might need to deal with both of these at the same time, as in $2(x + 5) = 3(2x - 4)$. Expand first and rearrange.

Test yourself

1 Rearrange and solve:

a) $2y + 1 = y + 5$ b) $3k - 7 = 2k + 3$

c) $4U + 1 = 2U - 3$ d) $3d - 2 = d + 3$

e) $10N = 3N + 21$

2 Expand and solve:

a) $4(x - 3) = 8$ b) $5(2 - r) = 15$

c) $2(2x + 5) = 10$ d) $2(7 - Q) = 8$

e) $5(3v - 8) = 5$

3 Expand, rearrange and solve:

a) $5(2b + 1) = 8b$ b) $2(3 + 7v) = 4v$

c) $2(s - 4) = 3(6s + 2)$ d) $5(F - 8) = 3(5 - 2F)$

e) $2(3h - 4) + 4(h + 5) = 3(2h + 8)$

BBC GCSE Check and Test: Maths

Check the facts

There are two types of equations involving fractions.

1 There is a fraction, but the unknown letter is on the top.
Use the standard rules for solving the equation.

Example: $\dfrac{5x}{3} + 2 = 7$ *(Write the equation down first.)*

$\dfrac{5x}{3} = 7 - 2 = 5$ *(Subtract 2 from both sides and simplify.)*

$5x = 5 \times 3 = 15$ *(Multiply both sides by 3 and simplify.)*

$x = 3$ *(Divide both sides by 5 and simplify.)*

2 The unknown letter is on the bottom. You need to multiply by
the denominator.

Example: $\dfrac{30}{4x+1} = 2$ *(Write the equation down first.)*

$30 = 2(4x+1)$ *(Multiply both sides by (4x + 1).)*

$2(4x+1) = 30$ *(Swap sides so x is on the left.)*

$4x+1 = 15$ *(Divide both sides by 2 and simplify.)*

$4x = 14$ *(Subtract 1 from both sides and simplify.)*

$x = 3.5$ *(Divide both sides by 4 and simplify.)*

Test yourself

Solve these equations.

1 a) $\dfrac{x}{2} = 3$ b) $\dfrac{h}{10} = 1$ c) $\dfrac{2M}{3} = 8$

   d) $\dfrac{d}{5} + 2 = 3$ e) $\dfrac{s}{10} - 7 = 3$

2 a) $\dfrac{p-7}{2} = 2$ b) $\dfrac{z+2}{5} = 1$ c) $\dfrac{2f-3}{7} = 1$

   d) $\dfrac{4x+6}{10} = 2$ e) $\dfrac{9-5x}{2} = -1$

3 a) $\dfrac{1}{a} = 2$ b) $\dfrac{6}{e} = 3$ c) $\dfrac{2}{x} + 1 = 3$

   d) $\dfrac{1}{w-1} = 4$ e) $\dfrac{1}{3-2w} = 3$

Check the facts

> Sometimes you can't find an exact solution to an
> equation but can find an approximation using
> trial and improvement or a decimal search.

This means trying likely answers in the equation to see how closely they fit.

Example: Solve the equation $x^5 + 5x - 10 = 3x^2$, correct to 2 d.p.

It's much easier if the right-hand side of the equation is a number to aim for, so rearrange it: $x^5 - 3x^2 + 5x = 10$. Record the results of the trials, together with your decisions, in a table like this:

Trial, x	$x^5 - 3x^2 + 5x$	Comments
1	3	Too small, so $x > 1$. Try $x = 2$.
2	30	Too big, so $x < 2$. x is between 1 and 2. Try numbers with 1 decimal place. Try 1.5, as it's halfway between 1 and 2
1.5	8.34375	Too small, so $x > 1.5$. Try 1.7, as it's about halfway between 1.5 and 2
1.7	14.02857	Too big, so $x < 1.7$. x is between 1.5 and 1.7 Try 1.6.
1.6	10.80576	Too big, so $x < 1.5$. x is between 1.5 and 1.6. Try numbers with 2 decimal places. Try 1.55, as it's halfway between 1.5 and 1.6.
1.55	9.48910...	Too small, so $x > 1.55$. Try 1.57, as it's about halfway between 1.55 and 1.6.
1.57	9.99419...	Too small, so $x > 1.57$.
1.58	10.25738...	Too big, so $x > 1.58$. x is between 1.57 and 1.58 It's one of these. You only need to know whether it's closer to 1.57 or 1.58. Trying 1.575 will decide
1.575	10.12488...	Too big, so $x < 1.575$.

So, $x = 1.58$ to 2 d.p.

Test yourself

Find at least one solution to these correct to 1 d.p.

1 These equations don't need to be rearranged.

a) $x^2 = 14$ b) $P^2 + P = 50$ c) $y^2 - 2y = 21$

d) $x^3 - 2x^2 = 5$ e) $x^3 - 10x = 1$ f) $2^x = 5$

2 These equations **do** need to be rearranged.

a) $x^2 + 11 = 9x$ b) $2z = 5 - z^2$

c) $n^5 + 2n = 3n^3 + 10n + 1$ d) $\sqrt{q} = 3q - 1$

e) $p^4 - 20 = p^2$ f) $a^2 - 1 = \sqrt{a}$

BBC GCSE Check and Test: Maths

Check the facts

A **formula** usually has a letter on the left-hand side of the equals sign, the **subject**, and an expression on the right-hand side. Formulae show connections between quantities. Any letter in a formula can become the subject by **rearranging** it. You follow the same rules as for solving equations: as long as you do the same thing to both sides of your formula, it is still true.

Example: Make F the subject of $C = \dfrac{5(F - 32)}{9}$.

$$\dfrac{5(F - 32)}{9} = C \quad \text{(Swap sides so the letter you want is on the left.)}$$

$$5(F - 32) = 9C \qquad \text{(Multiply both sides by 9.)}$$

$$F - 32 = \dfrac{9C}{5} \qquad \text{(Divide both sides by 5.)}$$

$$F = \dfrac{9C}{5} + 32 \qquad \text{(Add 32 to both sides.)}$$

Be very careful if the letter that's going to be the subject is on the **bottom of a fraction.** You need to **multiply** by the denominator.

Example: Make n the subject of $T = \dfrac{x}{n - 1}$.

$$T(n - 1) = x \qquad \text{(Multiply both sides by (n – 1).)}$$

$$n - 1 = \dfrac{x}{T} \qquad \text{(Divide both sides by T.)}$$

$$n = \dfrac{x}{T} + 1 \qquad \text{(Add 1 to both sides.)}$$

Test yourself

Make the coloured letter the subject of each formula.

1 $B = A - 30$
2 $d = 2r$
3 $S = \dfrac{n}{10} + 5$

4 $t = 2h + 40$
5 $e = a - b$
6 $f = pv$

7 $3x = 4y + 5$
8 $5x + 4y = 20$
9 $r = \sqrt{s}$

10 $C = 3r^2$
11 $t = \dfrac{4}{u}$
12 $G = g + 100$

13 $a = 5b$
14 $f = \dfrac{e}{3} - 3$
15 $q = 10p - 8$

16 $V = lbh$
17 $m = \dfrac{4}{k + 5}$
18 $w = 3(v + 1)$

19 $x = \sqrt{y + 1} - 1$
20 $Q = 4 - \dfrac{1}{2(R - X)}$

Algebra

Check the facts

Most things in mathematics can be given a name, usually a letter. Take a mathematical rule such as 'double the number and add 3'. Here is what the rule does to some numbers:

$1 \rightarrow \quad 2 \times 1 + 3 \ = 5$

$2 \rightarrow \quad 2 \times 2 + 3 \ = 7$

$5 \rightarrow \quad 2 \times 5 + 3 \ = 13$

$10 \rightarrow 2 \times 10 + 3 = 23$

A rule like this is called a **function**. Call this one f. Then the last line can be written $f(10) = 23$. This means 'start with 10 and use the rule: you get 23'.

To describe what the rule does, use it on a letter. This is called **defining** the function.

$x \rightarrow 2 \times x + 3 = 2x + 3$. So $f(x) = 2x + 3$.

You can work out the results of using the function by **substituting** numbers for x. Suppose another function g is defined by $g(x) = x^2 - 1$.

$g(1) = 1^2 - 1 = 1 - 1 = 0$

$g(4) = 4^2 - 1 = 16 - 1 = 15$

$g(11) = 11^2 - 1 = 121 - 1 = 120$

Test yourself

1 Suppose that $f(x) = 10x$, $g(x) = 2 - x$, $h(x) = \dfrac{1}{x-1}$ and $k(x) = x^3$.

Substitute to find the following.

a) $f(10)$

b) $g(2)$

c) $h(1)$

d) $k(5)$

e) $f(0.1)$

f) $g(0.1)$

g) $h(3)$

h) $k(1.1)$

i) $f(2) + f(3)$

j) $g(1) \times h(9)$

k) $\dfrac{k(6)}{k(2)}$

l) $[g(5)]^2$

 2 Use the letter x to write definitions for these functions.

a) f: multiply the number by 4, then subtract 2.

b) g: take the square of the number away from 9.

c) h: divide 2 by the number.

d) k: add 3 to the number. Add 1 to the number. Multiply these two answers together.

e) C: whatever the starting number, the answer is 1.

f) A: the number is the diameter of a circle. The function finds the area.

Algebra

Algebra

Check the facts

Simultaneous equations are pairs of equations with two unknown letters that are both true at the same time. This gives you enough information to find both letters.

The technique of elimination involves adding or subtracting the equations so that one of the letters disappears (is eliminated). Sometimes, you have to multiply one or both of the equations by something. This is to match numbers in order to add or subtract and eliminate.

> *Example:* Solve $2x + 5y = 18$
> $3x + 2y = 16$

You can't add or subtract. Neither x nor y will be eliminated.

h To match the numbers, multiply the first equation by 3 and the second by 2.

> $6x + 15y = 54$ $\qquad$ *($1^{st} \times 3$)*
> $6x + 4y = 32$ $\qquad$ *($2^{nd} \times 2$)*

Subtracting these will eliminate x:

> $6x + 15y - 6x - 4y = 54 - 32$.
> $\qquad 11y = 22 \qquad$ *(Simplify.)*
> $\qquad y = 2$.

Substitute this into one of the original equations to find $x = 4$.

The solution of the simultaneous equations is $x = 4, y = 2$.

Check by substituting into $3x + 2y = 16$: $12 + 4 = 16$ ✔

Test yourself

1 Solve these simultaneous equations by adding or substracting them.

a) $x + 2y = 6$
$\quad x - 2y = 4$

b) $3p - q = 9$
$\quad 5p + q = 7$

c) $2x + 3y = 2$
$\quad 5x + 3y = 14$

d) $3a + 4b = 45$
$\quad 3a + 2b = 33$

2 Solve these pairs of simultaneous equations. One or both equations
h need to be multiplied.

a) $3m + 4n = 10$
$\quad m - 2n = -10$

b) $5u - 6v = 17$
$\quad u + 3v = 16$

c) $5L + 6K = 6$
$\quad 3L + 2K = 10$

d) $9s + 2t = 8$
$\quad 2s + 9t = 36$

e) $7x + 2y = 2$
$\quad 2x - 3y = 22$

f) $5c - 6d = 7$
$\quad 4c - 9d = 14$

Check the facts

Algebraic substitution can be used to eliminate one of the letters from a pair of simultaneous equations.

Remember the equations from the last section . . .

> *Example:* Solve $2x + 5y = 18$
> $3x + 2y = 16$

Choose one of the letters and make it the subject of both equations (x, say).

$$2x + 5y = 18 \qquad\qquad 3x + 2y = 16$$
$$2x = 18 - 5y \qquad\qquad 3x = 16 - 2y$$
$$x = \frac{18 - 5y}{2} \qquad\qquad x = \frac{16 - 2y}{3}$$

Now substitute the value of x from one equation into the other.
This gives:

$$\frac{18 - 5y}{2} = \frac{16 - 2y}{3}$$

Solve this equation to find y, then find x by substitution.

Test yourself

Solve these equations.

1 $m - 2n = 1$
 $m + 2n = 13$

2 $3p - 4q = 27$
 $p + 4q = -7$

3 $j - 2k = 5$
 $j + 2k = 3$

4 $2x + y = 0$
 $3x - y = -5$

5 $7t - 8s = 34$
 $5t - 2s = 2$

6 $11D + 12E = -43$
 $5D + 4E = -5$

7 $5Q - 6R = 6$
 $3Q - 2R = 10$

8 $f + 4g = 3$
 $3f - 2g = -5$

Algebra

BBC GCSE Check and Test: Maths

Algebra

h

Check the facts

Each equation in a simultaneous pair has its own graph. Where the graphs cross (**intersect**), the solution can be found.

Example: Solve the simultaneous equations

$$x + 2y = 1, 2x + y = 8.$$

Make y the subject of both equations.

$$x + 2y = 1 \qquad\qquad 2x + y = 8$$
$$2y = 1 - x \qquad\qquad y = 8 - 2x$$
$$y = \frac{1 - x}{2}$$

Plot the graphs.

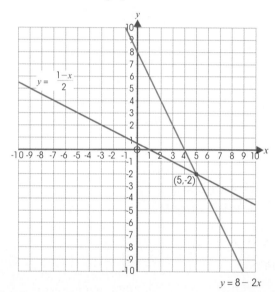

The graphs cross at $(5, -2)$.

Answer: The solution to the equations is $x = 5, y = -2$.

Test yourself

Plot graphs of each pair of equations to find the solution. A grid with $-10 \leqslant x, y \leqslant 10$ will be large enough for each. Check your solutions by elimination or substitution.

1 $x + y = 2$ $\qquad\qquad$ $2x - 3y = -5$
2 $x + 5y = 6$ $\qquad\qquad$ $2x + 3y = -2$
3 $x - 2y = 2$ $\qquad\qquad$ $2x + y = 7$
4 $3x - 2y = 7$ $\qquad\qquad$ $x + 4y = 0$
5 $5x - 6y = 57$ $\qquad\qquad$ $4x - 9y = 75$

Check the facts

Ranges of numbers are described using inequalities. You can illustrate an inequality on a number line.

There are four inequality symbols:

$>$ greater than	$\geqslant$ greater than or equal to
$<$ less than	$\leqslant$ less than or equal to

'All the numbers that are 3 or less' is described by the inequality $x \leqslant 3$ (or $3 \geqslant x$). The first number line shows the **integers** (whole numbers) that match this. The second shows what is allowed when **all** numbers are included.

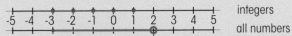

integers
all numbers

These lines show 'all the numbers that are greater than –3', $x > -3$ (or $-3 < x$). The open circle on the second line shows that you can get as close to –3 as you like, but –3 itself is not allowed.

integers
all numbers

Sometimes inequalities can be combined. Suppose that $x < 2$ and $x \geqslant -3$. This makes a range inequality, $-3 \leqslant x < 2$.

integers
all numbers

Test yourself

1 Draw a pair of number lines like those above to illustrate each inequality.

a) $x \geqslant 1$ b) $x \leqslant 0$ c) $x > -2$

d) $4 > x$ e) $x > 0.5$ f) $0 \leqslant x \leqslant 3$

g) $-5 < x \leqslant -1$ h) $2 - x < 3$

2 Write an inequality to match each number line.

a)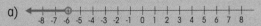

b)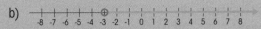

c)

d)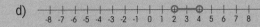

Algebra

Check the facts

> You solve equations to find an unknown number.
> You can solve inequalities to find a range of numbers.

Compare these:

$2x - 5 = 7$	*(Write down the question.)*	$2x - 5 > 7$
$2x = 12$	*(Add 5 to both sides.)*	$2x > 12$
$x = 6$	*(Divide both sides by 2.)*	$x > 6$

As long as you do the same thing to both sides of an inequality, it will be valid, **except** if you multiply or divide by a negative number. In that case, the direction of the inequality is **reversed**.

Example: Solve the inequality $4 - 3x \geqslant 10$.

$4 - 3x \geqslant 10$	*(Write down the question.)*
$-3x \geqslant 6$	*(Subtract 4 from both sides.)*
$x \leqslant -2$	*(Divide by −3, so reverse inequality.)*

You can solve a range inequality by doing the same thing to all three parts.

Example: Solve the inequality $12 < 4x + 2 \leqslant 20$.

$12 < 4x + 2 \leqslant 20$	*(Write down the question.)*
$10 < 4x \leqslant 18$	*(Subtract 2.)*
$2.5 < x \leqslant 4.5$	*(Divide by 4.)*

Test yourself

Solve each inequality, then draw a number line to illustrate it.

1. $2x + 1 \leqslant 9$ (integers)
2. $4x - 1 \leqslant 3$ (all numbers)
3. $3x - 2 > 4$ (integers)
4. $6x + 4 \geqslant 4$ (all numbers)
5. $\frac{x}{3} \leqslant -2$ (all numbers)
6. $2 < x - 1 < 4$ (integers)
7. $-2 < 3x + 1 \leqslant 1$ (all numbers)
8. $-4 < 2x < -2$ (integers)
9. $1 - 2x \geqslant 7$ (all numbers)
10. $0 < 2(3 - x) < 10$ (all numbers)

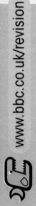

Check the facts

> **Multiples** of a number are in its multiplication table.

Examples: Multiples of 2 are the even numbers.
Multiples of 10 are 10, 20, 30, 40, etc.

> **Factors** of a number are other numbers that divide into it without leaving a remainder.

Example: The factors of 12 are 1, 2, 3, 4, 6 and 12.
Factors come in pairs: $1 \times 12 = 12$, $2 \times 6 = 12$, $3 \times 4 = 12$.

The only exception to this rule is for **square** numbers, where one factor pairs with itself.

Example: The factors of 25 are 1, 5 and 25. $1 \times 25 = 25$ and $5 \times 5 = 25$.

A **prime** number only has two factors: 1 and the number itself. The first few prime numbers are 2, 3, 5, 7, 11, 13, 17, 19, 23, . . . A number that isn't prime is **composite**.

Test yourself

1 From the cloud of numbers, pick out the ones that are:
a) factors of 10   b) multiples of 7   c) square numbers
d) factors of 72   e) multiples of 3   f) factors of 84
g) prime numbers

2 Write down all the factors of:
a) 24   b) 36   c) 77   d) 125   e) 1100

3 Test these numbers to see if they are prime or composite:
a) 123   b) 125   c) 147   d) 153   e) 199

Patterns and relationships

BBC GCSE Check and Test: Maths

Check the facts

Any number can be written as a product of prime factors. This means writing it using only prime numbers multiplied together.

Firstly, break your number down into any two factors, then break these down, and so on.

Example: Write 24 as a product of prime factors.

$$24 = 6 \times 4 \qquad \text{(Break into two factors.)}$$
$$24 = \mathbf{2 \times 3} \times 4 \qquad \text{(Break first factor down.)}$$
$$24 = 2 \times 3 \times \mathbf{2 \times 2} \text{ (Break second factor down.)}$$

Now there are only prime numbers in the breakdown.

$$24 = 2 \times 2 \times 2 \times 3 \text{ (Rearrange factors in order of size.)}$$
$$24 = 2^3 \times 3. \qquad \text{(Use indices for repeated factors.)}$$

Another method is to divide by prime numbers repeatedly until only a prime number is left.

Example: Write 450 as a product of prime factors.

```
                        5
            5)    2    5
            3)    7    5
        3)    2    2    5
        2)    4    5    0
```

The breakdown is $2 \times 3 \times 3 \times 5 \times 5 = 2 \times 3^2 \times 5^2$.

Test yourself

1 What numbers are made by these prime factor products?
   a) 2×3^2
   b) $2^3 \times 5$
   c) $2 \times 3 \times 7$
   d) 5×11^2
   e) $2 \times 11 \times 13$
   f) $2^2 \times 3^2 \times 5^2$
   g) $2^5 \times 29$
   h) $2 \times 5^2 \times 17$
   i) $3^4 \times 11$
   j) $11 \times 13 \times 19^3$

2 Write these numbers as products of prime factors.
   a) 36   b) 22   c) 59   d) 75
   e) 100   f) 123   g) 144   h) 289
   i) 667   j) 668

Check the facts

Factors of 36: 1, **2**, 3, **4**, 6, 9, 12, 18, 36.

Factors of 40: 1, **2**, **4**, 5, 8, 10, 20, 40.

The coloured numbers are in both lists. They are the **common factors** of 36 and 40. The largest one is **4**. 4 is the largest number that will divide into both 36 and 40. 4 is the **highest common factor (HCF)** of 36 and 40.

Multiples of 6: 6, 12, 18, **24**, 30, 36, 42, **48**, 54, 60,...

Multiples of 8: 8, 16, **24**, 32, 40, **48**, 56, 64, 72, 80,...

The coloured numbers are in both lists. They are the **common multiples** of 6 and 8. The smallest one is **24**.

This is the smallest number that both 6 and 8 will divide into. 24 is the **lowest common multiple (LCM)** of 6 and 8.

Prime factors are related to both HCF and LCM. Consider 540 and 1008.

$$540 = 2^2 \times 3^3 \times 5$$
$$1008 = 2^4 \times 3^2 \times 7$$

To find the HCF, use the smallest power of each prime factor: 2^2, 3^2, no 5s and no 7s: HCF = $2^2 \times 3^2 = 36$.

The LCM comes from the largest power of each prime factor: 2^4, 3^3, a 5 and a 7: LCM = $2^4 \times 3^3 \times 5 \times 7 = 15\ 120$.

h

Test yourself

1 Find the HCF of:
a) 15 and 20   b) 36 and 48   c) 45 and 63
d) 54 and 90   e) 150 and 120   f) 60 and 105
g) 84 and 147   h) 18, 24 and 42 i) 75, 125 and 200
j) 135, 189 and 108

2 Find the LCM of:
a) 6 and 9   b) 10 and 15   c) 6 and 10
d) 21 and 35   e) 15 and 25   f) 16 and 18
g) 75 and 125   h) 7, 8 and 12   i) 24, 12, and 16
j) 10, 12 and 15

3 Use the prime factor method to find the HCF and LCM of these numbers:
a) 2250 and 60   b) 54 and 1764
c) 1575 and 180   d) 1479 and 1482
e) 2310, 12 100 and 441

h

Patterns and relationships

BBC GCSE Check and Test: Maths

Check the facts

Number patterns grow according to a rule. There are certain patterns you need to be able to recognise.

Even numbers: 2, 4, 6, 8, 10, ...

Odd numbers: 1, 3, 5, 7, 9, ...

Square numbers: 1, 4, 9, 16, 25, ...

Cube numbers: 1, 8, 27, 81, 125, ...

Triangular numbers: 1, 3, 6, 10, 15, ...

Powers of 2: 2, 4, 8, 16, 32, ...

Multiples of a given number n: n, $2n$, $3n$, $4n$, $5n$, ...

Powers of a given number x: x, x^2, x^3, x^4, x^5, ...

Test yourself

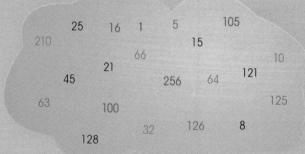

25   16   1   5   105

210   15

          66

    21

45   256   64   121

63   100   125

128   32   126   8

10

From the cloud of numbers, pick out the ones that are:

1 even numbers

2 triangular numbers

3 square numbers

4 odd numbers

5 multiples of 21

6 cube numbers

7 powers of 5

8 powers of 2

Check the facts

Sequences are made up of a succession of **terms**. Each term has a **position** in the sequence: **1st, 2nd**, etc. A linear sequence is one where the difference between terms is always the same number, such as 2, 5, 8, 11, 14, . . .

Using n to stand for the position in the sequence and T to stand for the term, every linear sequence has a formula. First make a difference table. Label the positions.

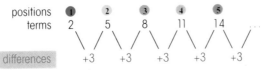

This shows that the terms count up 3 times as fast as the positions, so a first attempt at the formula could be $T = 3n$. This won't work because $T = 3n$ gives the terms 3, 6, 9, 12, 15, . . . You need to subtract 1 from each term to begin on 2 instead of 3. So the formula is $T = 3n - 1$.

With a formula, it's easy to find terms a long way into the sequence. For example, the 100th term of this sequence is $3 \times 100 - 1 = 299$.

Sequences that are **descending** instead of **ascending** have negative differences.

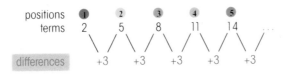

The formula is $T = -2n + 12$, or $T = 12 - 2n$.

Test yourself

1 Generate the first five terms of each sequence.
   a) $T = 3n + 2$ b) $T = 10n - 4$
   c) $T = 12 - n$ d) $T = 30 - 5n$
   e) $T = 0.5n$ f) $T = 1.5n - 1.5$
   g) $T = -11n - 6$ h) $T = 1.01n + 0.8$

2 Find the formula for each sequence. Calculate the 10th and 100th terms.
   a) 5, 7, 9, 11, 13, . . .   b) 0, 3, 6, 9, 12, . . .
   c) 6, 11, 16, 21, 26, . . .   d) 7.5, 14.5, 21.5, 28.5, . . .
   e) 5, 3, 1, −1, −3, . . .   f) 18, 28, 38, 48, 58, . . .
   g) 3.1, 3.2, 3.3, 3.4, 3.5, . . .   h) −4, −3, −2, −1, 0, . . .

Check the facts

Quadratic sequences have formulae of the form $T = an^2 + bn + c$. To analyse quadratic sequences, look at the **second** difference row.

This sequence is the square numbers, $T = n^2$.

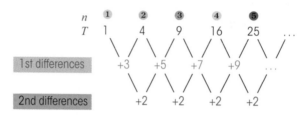

The second differences are all +2. The rule is: **for every 2 in the second differences, there is an n^2 in the formula**. Once the number of n^2 is known, there is a linear part left to find. This is how to do it.

Example: find the formula for the sequence 0, 11, 28, 51, 80, ...

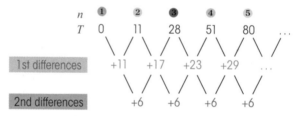

The second differences are all +6. That means that you need $3n^2$ in the formula. To find the linear part, take the terms of $3n^2$ away from the terms of the original sequence.

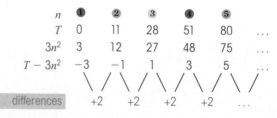

$2n - 5$ generates the terms −3, −1, 1, 3, 5, ... So the original sequence is T $= 3n^2 + 2n - 5$.

Test yourself

Find the formula for each sequence. Calculate the 10th and 100th terms.

1 6, 11, 18, 27, 38, ...   **2** 3, 6, 11, 18, 27, ...

3 2, 6, 14, 26, 42, ...   **4** 3, 3, 1, −3, −9, ...

Check the facts

Power sequences are made from powers of numbers.

Examples: $T = 2^n$ 2, 4, 8, 16, 32, ...

$T = 10^n$ 10, 100, 1000, 10 000, ...

Sequences of fractions

$T = n + 2$ gives this sequence: 3, 4, 5, 6, 7,...

$T = 3n - 1$ gives this sequence: 2, 5, 8, 11, 14,...

If you use these numbers to make fractions you get this

sequence: $\frac{3}{2}, \frac{4}{5}, \frac{5}{8}, \frac{6}{11}, \frac{7}{14}, \dots$

So the formula for the fraction sequence is just $T = \dfrac{n + 2}{3n - 1}$.

Sequences of products

Look at this sequence: 0, 15, 56, 135, ...

0 $= 0 \times 3$, **15** $= 3 \times 5$, **56** $= 8 \times 7$, **135** $= 15 \times 9$.

Each term is the product of two sequences.

The first sequence is 0, 3, 8, 15, ...: $T = n^2 - 1$.

The second sequence is 3, 5, 7, 9, ...: $T = 2n + 1$.

To get the product, just multiply the two parts:

$$T = (n^2 - 1)(2n + 1).$$

Test yourself

1 Find the formula for each sequence. Calculate the 10th and 20th terms.

a) $\dfrac{1}{1}, \dfrac{2}{3}, \dfrac{3}{5}, \dfrac{4}{7}, \dfrac{5}{9}, \dots$ b) $\dfrac{2}{3}, \dfrac{4}{5}, \dfrac{6}{7}, \dfrac{8}{9}, \dfrac{10}{11}, \dots$

c) $\dfrac{4}{4}, \dfrac{7}{10}, \dfrac{10}{16}, \dfrac{13}{22}, \dfrac{16}{28}, \dots$ d) $\dfrac{1}{11}, \dfrac{4}{21}, \dfrac{9}{31}, \dfrac{16}{41}, \dfrac{25}{51}, \dots$

e) $\dfrac{7}{1}, \dfrac{6}{4}, \dfrac{5}{9}, \dfrac{4}{16}, \dfrac{3}{25}, \dots$ f) $\dfrac{10}{13}, \dfrac{9}{16}, \dfrac{8}{19}, \dfrac{7}{22}, \dfrac{6}{25}, \dots$

2 Find the formula for each sequence. Calculate the 10th and 20th terms.

a) 6, 15, 28, 45, 66, ...

$(3 \times 2, 5 \times 3, 7 \times 4, 9 \times 5, 11 \times 6, \dots)$

b) 16, 35, 60, 91, 128, ...

$(4 \times 4, 5 \times 7, 6 \times 10, 7 \times 13, 8 \times 16, \dots)$

c) 9, 56, 171, 384, 725, ...

$(1 \times 9, 4 \times 14, 9 \times 19, 16 \times 24, 25 \times 29, \dots)$

d) 0.6, 5.6, 21.6, 57.6, 125, ...

$(1 \times 0.6, 8 \times 0.7, 27 \times 0.8, 64 \times 0.9, 125 \times 1, \dots)$

Check the facts

> The metric system of units, like our number system,
> is based on tens. The basic units of length, mass and capacity
> are the metre **(m)**, gram **(g)** and litre **(l)**.

Different sizes of unit for different purposes are made by adding **prefixes** to the basic units.

prefix	milli- (m)	centi- (c)	hecto- (h)	kilo- (k)
meaning	$\frac{1}{1000}$	$\frac{1}{100}$	100	1000

Also, 1000 kg = 1 tonne (t).

The only exception to this rule is for **time**.
60 seconds = 1 minute, 60 minutes = 1 hour and 24 hours = 1 day, though milliseconds (ms) and centiseconds (cs) are sometimes used.

Other metric units exist. **Area** is usually measured in square metres (m^2), etc., but land is measured in ares (100 ares = 1 hectare). Note that 1 cm^2 = 100 mm^2, not 10 mm^2.

Volume is measured in m^3. 1 cm^3 = 1 ml. Note that 1 cm^3 = 1000 mm^3, not 10 or 100 mm^3.

Electrical units such as volts (V), amps (A), ohms (Ω), watts (W) and joules (J) all take metric prefixes. Units of **computer** storage (bytes) take prefixes too, including mega- (M) for a million and giga- (G) for a billion.

To convert measurements from one unit to another, remember that changing to a **smaller** unit means more of them, so **multiply**. Changing to a larger unit means less of them, so **divide**.

Test yourself

1 What instruction is missing from each sentence?
Example: To change cm to mm, × 10.

a) To change m to cm, ...

b) To change ml to cl, ...

c) ... t to kg, ...

d) ... t to g, ...

e) ... g to kg, ...

f) ...cl to l, ...

g) ... km to cm, ...

h) ... V to mV, ...

2 Each line represents the same measurement. Fill in the blanks.

a) **?** mm = **?** cm = 2 m = **?** km

b) **?** ml = 6 cl = **?** l

c) 8 g = **?** kg = **?** t

d) **?** mm = 48 cm = **?** m = **?** km

e) **?** mm^2 = **?** cm^2 = 1 m^2

Check the facts

Older-style units called **imperial** units are still quite common. They are **not**, in general, based on tens.

> **Length: 12 inches (in) = 1 foot (ft); 3 ft = 1 yard (yd);
> 1760 yd = 1 mile (mi).**
>
> **Mass: 16 ounces (oz) = 1 pound (lb);
> 14 lb = 1 stone (st); 2240 lb = 1 ton.**
>
> **Capacity: 20 fluid ounces (fl oz) = 1 pint (pt).
> 2 pt = 1 quart (qt). 4 qt = 1 gallon (gal).**

It helps to know the rough equivalents in the metric system. These are the most useful:

> **Length: 1 in ≈ 2.54 cm; 1 ft ≈ 30 cm; 1 mile ≈ 1.6 km.**
>
> **Mass: 1 oz ≈ 28 g; 1 lb ≈ 0.45 kg; 1 ton ≈ 1 t.**
>
> **Capacity: 1 fl oz ≈ 29 ml; 1 pt ≈ 0.57 l; 1 gal ≈ 4.6 l.**

Test yourself

1 Convert to metric:

a) 8 oz

b) 5 mi

c) 15 gal

d) $\frac{1}{2}$ in

e) 6 ft

f) $2\frac{1}{2}$ pt

g) 12 fl oz

h) 12 st

i) 1 in^2

j) 3 lb

2 Convert to imperial:

a) 1 mm

b) 1 cm

c) 1 m

d) 1 km

e) 1 g

f) 1 kg

g) 1 ml

h) 1 cl

i) 1 l

j) 1 m^2

Measurement and mensuration

BBC GCSE Check and Test: Mahts

Check the facts

In theory, if you had an accurate enough ruler, you could measure the length of an object as precisely as you wanted to. Practically, there's always a limit to how accurate you can be. The range of values allowed can be written using an inequality:

minimum ≤ measurement < maximum.

Suppose the length L of a piece of wire is 67 mm, to the nearest mm.

67mm to nearest mm

Anything less than 66.5 mm would round down to 66 mm. Anything 67.5 mm and above would round up to 68 mm. So $66.5 ≤ L < 67.5$.

If L is given to the nearest 0.1 mm (1 d.p.) instead, then
$66.95 ≤ L , 67.05$.

If you have to do a calculation with measurements like this, use these rules:

To get the		To get the	
maximum	max + max	**minimum**	min + min
	max − min		min − max
answer	max × max	answer	min × min
	max ÷ min		min ÷ max

Example: A rectangle is 6 cm by 4 cm. The measurements are accurate to 1 d.p. Find the minimum and maximum area of the rectangle.

Length $l ≈ 6$ cm. $5.95 ≤ l < 6.05$.
Width $w ≈ 4$ cm. $3.95 ≤ w < 4.05$.
Maximum area = $6.05 × 4.05 = 24.5025$ cm^2.
Minimum area = $5.95 × 3.95 = 23.5025$ cm^2.

Test yourself

1 Write inequalities using x to match these measurements.
   a) 8 cm to the nearest cm   b) 8 cm to the nearest mm
   c) 15 kg to the nearest kg   d) 40 l to 1 d.p.
   e) 500 kg to the nearest 10 kg f) 2000 m to 2 s.f.

2 Write inequalities for the perimeter and area of these rectangles. The accuracy of the measurements is given in brackets.
   a) 5 cm × 2 cm (1 s.f.)   b) 20 cm by 30 cm (1 s.f.)
   c) 7.5 cm by 6.3 cm (1 d.p.)

Check the facts

Time calculations are more difficult than those for length, mass, and so on, because of the relationship between the time units. Remember, 60s = 1m, 60m = 1h and 24h = 1 day.

There are two ways to tackle time calculations. Suppose you wanted to add two lengths of time together: Say, 1h 35m 55s + 2h 42m 36s.

Example: The first way is to add up each unit separately to give 3h 77m 91s. The excess seconds and minutes need to be 'carried' up to the minutes and hours.
3h 77m 91s = 3h 78m 31s = 4h 18m 31s.

Example: The second way is to convert everything to the smallest unit, do the calculation, then convert back.
1h 35m 55s = (3600 + 35 × 60 + 55) = 5755s.
2h 42m 36s = (2 × 3600 + 42 × 60 + 36) = 9756s.

The total is 15 511s. Dividing 15 511 by 60 gives 258 remainder 31s. Dividing 258 by 60 gives 4 remainder 18m, so the answer is 4h 18m 31s as before. This looks like more trouble, and is, for most calculations, but you must use it for division.

Warning! Most calculators aren't equipped to handle time. Some people would quite happily add 2m 55s to 5m 48s by typing

| 2 | • | 5 | 5 | + | 5 | • | 4 | 8 | = | 8.03 |

and give the answer as 8m 3s. The correct answer is 8m 33s, of course!

Test yourself

1 These are the start and end readings for a video recorder, and the times recorded. Complete the table.

Start	0:45:31		3:23:42	4:44:38
Duration	32:00	47:36		2:36:55
Finish		5:12:14	5:18:45	

2 A robot takes 13 minutes 47 seconds to complete a work cycle.
   a) How long does it take to complete:
      i) 3 cycles   ii) 10 cycles?
   b) How many cycles does it complete in a 12 hour period?

3 How many seconds are there in a year?

Measurement and mensuration

BBC GCSE Check and Test: Mahts

Check the facts

> **Units of speed are metres per second (m/s), kilometres per hour (km/h), miles per hour (mph), etc.**

Usually, the speed of an object is not constant, but varies during a journey. It is only possible to work out the average speed.

The formula is speed = distance ÷ time. This can be rearranged to give distance = speed × time and time = distance ÷ speed. Remember these with the 'd-s-t triangle'.

To use it, cover up the letter you want to work out: the triangle gives the formula. This shows 'time = distance ÷ speed'.

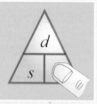

Warning! You can only use these formulae when the units match. It's no good trying to divide km/h by miles! If necessary, convert first.

Test yourself

1 Convert these speeds.
a) 10 km/s to km/h   b) 22 m/s to cm/s
c) 50 km/h to m/s   d) 72 m/s to km/h
e) 88 km/h to mph (Use 1 mile = 1.6 km)

2 Complete the table for these journeys.

Distance	Time	Speed
5000 km	2 hours	km/h
1 km	$\frac{1}{4}$ hour	km/h
	4 hours	20 km/h
400 m	5 seconds	km/h
	1 hour	12 m/s
250 m		12.5 m/s
	20 seconds	36 000 km/h
3 km		20 m/s
7 km		35 cm/s
15 cm	$\frac{1}{10}$ second	km/h

Check the facts

The sides of a rectangle are called by many different names, including length, width, height and base.

> Using *l* for length and *w* for width, the area
> A of a rectangle is given by $A = lw$.
> The perimeter is $P = 2l + 2w$ or $2(l + w)$.
> For squares, the sides are all the same, so $A = l^2$ and $P = 4l$.

> **To find an unknown side in a rectangle, divide:**
>
> $$l = \frac{A}{w} \quad \text{or} \quad w = \frac{A}{l}.$$
>
> **To find the side length of a square, square root the area:**
>
> $$(l = \sqrt{A}).$$

Compound shapes are made by adding areas of shapes together or by subtracting one shape from another.

Test yourself

1 Find the areas and perimeters of these rectangles.

a)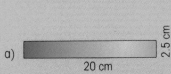
20 cm
2.5 cm

b) 400 m
2 km

2 Find the missing measurements.

a)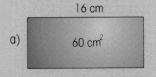
16 cm
60 cm^2

b) 440 cm^2
0.8 m

3 Find the areas.

a)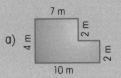
7 m
4 m
2 m
2 m
10 m

b)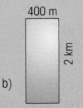
20 cm
12 cm
2 cm
4 cm
7 cm

Measurement and mensuration

BBC GCSE Check and Test: Mahts

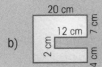

Check the facts

Triangles, parallelograms and trapezia all share an important measurement: the perpendicular height. These are the area formulae:

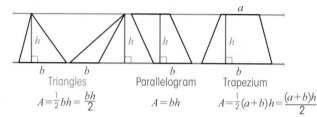

Triangles

$A = \frac{1}{2}bh = \frac{bh}{2}$

Parallelogram

$A = bh$

Trapezium

$A = \frac{1}{2}(a+b)h = \frac{(a+b)h}{2}$

Be very careful when you are also given slanting sides in these shapes. They are not part of area calculations, but are used in finding the perimeter.

Test yourself

1 Find the areas of these.

a) 12 cm, 20 cm

b) 4.5 mm, 4 mm

c) 7.3 m, 10 m

d) 4.5 km, 1.2 km

e) 130 m, 81 m, 30 m

2 These are compound shapes. Find their areas.

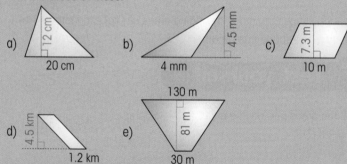

a) 7 m, 5 m, 4 m

b) 3 cm, 6 cm, 6 cm, 6 cm

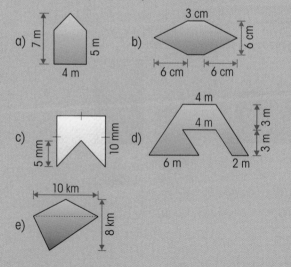

c) 5 mm, 10 mm

d) 4 m, 4 m, 6 m, 2 m, 3 m, 3 m

e) 10 km, 8 km

Check the facts

The circumference of a circle is a little more than 3 times the diameter. The exact number of times is very important in mathematics and has been given a special name: **pi**. This is pronounced 'pie' and is written using the Greek letter 'p', π. $\pi \approx 3.142$. There should be a $\boxed{\pi}$ key on your calculator.

> **circumference = $\pi \times$ diameter, $C = \pi d$.**

When a wheel turns once (makes one **revolution**), the distance moved by whatever it's attached to (e.g. a car, bike, and so on) is the same as the circumference of the wheel.

> **To find the length of an arc of a circle, multiply the circumference by the fraction of the circle required.**

If the angle is $x°$, the fraction is $\dfrac{x}{360}$.

Test yourself

1 Complete the table. Each row represents one circle. Round your answers appropriately.

Diameter	Radius	Circumference
12 cm		
4 m		
	7 mm	
		10 m
12 400 km		
		3 mm
	62 cm	
		75 km

2 Jason's journey to school is 3.5 km. His cycle wheels turn 1860 times during this journey.
   a) What is the diameter of a cycle wheel?
   b) Jason cycles at an average speed of 20 km/h. How many revolutions per minute do the wheels make?

3 Work out the length of each arc.

a)

b)

Measurement and mensuration

BBC GCSE Check and Test: Mahts

Check the facts

The area of the circle is a little over 3 times the tinted square: actually, π times. The area of the square is r^2, so the area of the circle is $A = \pi r^2$.

To find the radius if you know the area, divide by π, then square root.

To find the area of a sector of a circle, multiply the area of the whole circle by the fraction of the circle required.

If the angle is $x°$, the fraction is $\dfrac{x}{360}$.

Test yourself

1 Complete the table. Each row represents one circle. Round your answers appropriately.

Diameter	Radius	Circumference	Area
10 m			
8 cm			
	2 cm		
		13 mm	
			40 km^2
		21 m	
	50 m		
			12 cm^2

2 Find the areas.

a)
2 m

b)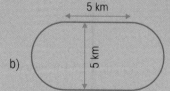
5 km
5 km

c)
6 cm
3 cm

d)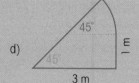
45°
45°
1 m
3 m

Check the facts

> The volume of a solid shape is the amount of 3-dimensional space it occupies.

There are four basic volume formulae:

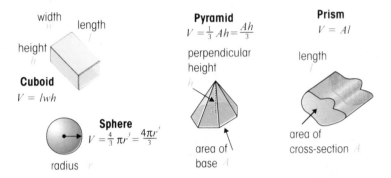

Cuboid
$V = lwh$

Sphere
$V = \frac{4}{3}\pi r^3 = \frac{4\pi r^3}{3}$

radius r

Pyramid
$V = \frac{1}{3}Ah = \frac{Ah}{3}$

perpendicular height h

area of base A

Prism
$V = Al$

length l

area of cross-section A

Note that cylinders are prisms with circular cross-sections, so for a cylinder $V = \pi r^2 l$.

Cones are pyramids with a circular base, so $V = \frac{1}{3}\pi r^2 h = \dfrac{\pi r^2 h}{3}$.

Remember that the capacity of a container is just its volume, written in capacity units.

$1\ cm^3 = 1\ ml$, $1\ l = 1000\ cm^3$, $1000\ l = 1\ m^3$.

Test yourself

1 Find the volume of each object.

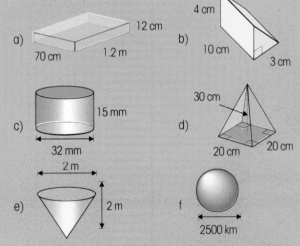

a) 12 cm, 70 cm, 1.2 m

b) 4 cm, 10 cm, 3 cm

c) 15 mm, 32 mm

d) 30 cm, 20 cm, 20 cm

e) 2 m, 2 m

f) 2500 km

2 A juice carton is 28 mm × 72 mm × 95 mm. How many ml of juice does it hold?

Measurement and mensuration

BBC GCSE Check and Test: Mahts

Measurement and mensuration

Check the facts

The surface area of a solid object is the combined area of all the faces on the outside. Curved surfaces on spheres, cones and cylinders form part of the surface area too.

For a prism, with area of cross-section A, the rectangles joining the two ends add up to the perimeter P of the end multiplied by the length of the prism, so the total surface area $S = 2A + Pl$. This works for a cylinder, of course, giving $S = 2\pi r^2 + 2\pi rl = 2\pi r(r + l)$.

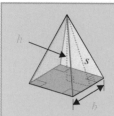

For a pyramid, the height of the triangle on each side has to be found from the perpendicular height of the apex using Pythagoras' theorem. The area of the triangle shown is $\frac{1}{2}bs$.

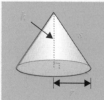

Cones need an extra measurement, the slant height s. The curved surface is πrs, so the total surface area is $\pi r^2 + \pi rs = \pi r^2(r + s)$.

The surface area of a sphere is $4\pi r^2$.

Test yourself

Find the surface area of:

1 A cuboid 2.5 cm $\times$ 6 cm $\times$ 8 cm.

2 A 10 cm cube.

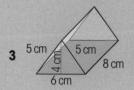

3 5 cm, 5 cm, 4 cm, 8 cm, 6 cm

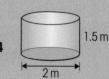

4 1.5 m, 2 m

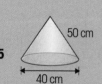

5 50 cm, 40 cm

6 A sphere with diameter 30 m.

7 A pyramid with a 10 cm square base and perpendicular height 12 cm.

www.bbc.co.uk/revision

Measurement and mensuration

Check the facts

All types of measurement are built up from the basic dimensions of length, mass and time. If you want to know what an expression represents, you can perform a **dimensional analysis.**

- Replace all lengths in the formula by the dimension letter L, masses by M and times by T.

- Remove all null quantities by crossing them out. Null quantities are numbers (including π) and any letters that just stand for numbers, fractions, angles, and trig functions, but **not** indices on letters.

- Simplify the expression as much as possible. If any more null quantities appear, get rid of them. The final result tells you the dimension of the original expression.

L = length, L^2 = area, L^3 = volume, and so on.

Example: What is the dimension of the expression $2\pi r^2 + 2\pi rl$?

$$2\pi r^2 + 2\pi rl \rightarrow 2\pi L^2 + 2\pi LL \quad \textit{(change to dimension letters)}$$

$$\rightarrow L^2 + LL \qquad\qquad \textit{(remove null quantities)}$$

$$\rightarrow L^2 + L^2 \rightarrow 2L^2 \qquad\qquad \textit{(simplify)}$$

$$\rightarrow L^2 \qquad\qquad \textit{(remove null quantities: finished)}$$

From the table, this is an **area** expression.

If you end up with a mixed expression such as $L + L^2$, the original expression was meaningless.

Test yourself

BBC GCSE Check and Test: Mahts

In these expressions, n is a number, θ and α are angles and A is an area. All other letters are lengths. Find the dimension of each formula.

1 ab	**2** $2a + 2b$	**3** $ab\sin\theta$
4 $\frac{1}{2}bh$	**5** $\frac{1}{2}(a+b+c)$	**6** nb
7 πr^2	**8** 2π	**9** abc
10 $2(bc + ac + ab)$	**11** $\pi r^2 h$	**12** $Al\sin\theta$
13 $2a^2b^2$	**14** $x^2 + y^2 + z^2$	**15** $\dfrac{x(a+b)}{3}$
16 $rh + l$	**17** $\frac{1}{4}(ab^2 + ba^2)$	**18** $\dfrac{\pi h^2(3r - h)}{3}$
19 $2nr\cos\alpha$	**20** $l^2 + 2r$	**21** $\sqrt{x^2 + y^2}$
22 $\dfrac{4\pi r^3}{3}$	**23** $2s^2 + \pi rl$	**24** πab^2

Check the facts

Whenever lines meet or **intersect**, the angles they make follow certain rules.

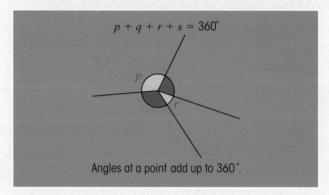

$a + b = 180°$

Adjacent angles on a straight line add up to 180°.

$p + q + r + s = 360°$

Angles at a point add up to 360°.

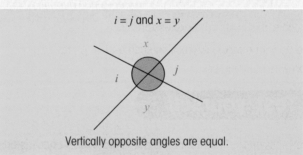

$i = j$ and $x = y$

Vertically opposite angles are equal.

Test yourself

Find all the angles marked with letters.

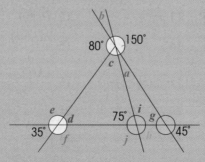

Check the facts

Three types of relationship between angles are produced when a line called a **transversal** crosses a pair of parallel lines.

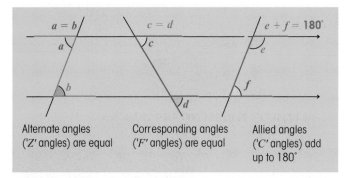

| Alternate angles ('Z' angles) are equal | Corresponding angles ('F' angles) are equal | Allied angles ('C' angles) add up to 180° |

Test yourself

1

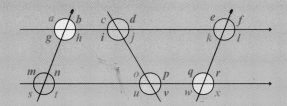

Identify the relationship between each pair of angles

Example: *h* and *t*: *h* = *t* (corresponding angles)

a) *g* and *n*   b) *c* and *o*   c) *k* and *q*   d) *i* and *p*

e) *u* and *v*   f) *a* and *h*   g) *b* and *f*   h) *n* and *q*

i) *e* and *h*   j) *h* and *l*

2 Find the angles marked with letters. Give reasons, i.e. which relationship you used.

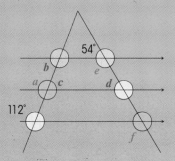

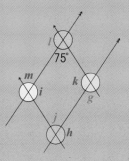

Shape and space

BBC GCSE Check and Test: Maths

Check the facts

The angle sum of a triangle is always 180°.

Any exterior angle of a triangle can be found by adding the two 'opposite' interior angles:

Here are the important triangles and their properties.

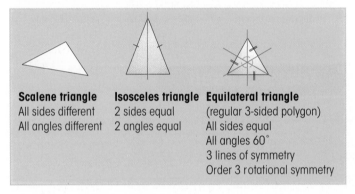

Scalene triangle
All sides different
All angles different

Isosceles triangle
2 sides equal
2 angles equal

Equilateral triangle
(regular 3-sided polygon)
All sides equal
All angles 60°
3 lines of symmetry
Order 3 rotational symmetry

To construct a triangle with given sides:

Test yourself

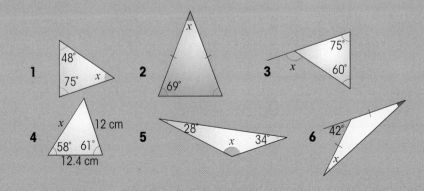

1. $48°$, $75°$, x

2. x, $69°$

3. x, $75°$, $60°$

4. x, 12 cm, $58°$, $61°$, 12.4 cm

5. $28°$, x, $34°$

6. $42°$, x

Check the facts

Here are the important quadrilaterals and their properties.

General quadrilateral
No special features

Concave or re-entrant quadrilateral
1 reflex angle

Kite
2 pairs of adjacent sides equal
1 pair of opposite angles equal
1 line of symmetry
Diagonals intersect at 90°

Trapezium
1 pair of parallel sides

Isosceles Trapezium
1 pair of parallel sides
1 pair of opposite sides equal
2 pairs of adjacent angles equal
1 line of symmetry

Parallelogram
2 pairs of parallel sides
2 pairs of opposite sides equal
2 pairs of opposite angles equal
Order 2 rotational symmetry

Rhombus
2 pairs of parallel sides
All sides equal
2 pairs of opposite angles equal
2 lines of symmetry
Order 2 rotational symmetry
Diagonals intersect at 90°

Rectangle
2 pairs of parallel sides
2 pairs of opposite sides equal
All angles 90°
2 lines of symmetry
Order 2 rotational symmetry
Diagonals intersect at 90°

Square (regular 4-sided polygon)
2 pairs of parallel sides
All sides equal
All angles 90°
4 lines of symmetry
Order 4 rotational symmetry
Diagonals intersect at 90°

Test yourself

Find the angles and lengths marked with letters.

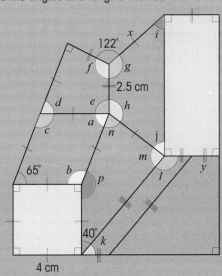

Check the facts

All polygons have **interior** and **exterior** angles. The interior angles are what you normally call just 'the angles'.

To find the **exterior** angles, you need to extend or **produce** the sides of the polygon.
An **interior** angle and its **exterior** angle always add up to 180°.

The exterior angles of a polygon always add up to exactly 360°.

The angle sum of a polygon is the total of all the interior angles.

Number of sides	Angle sum
3 (triangle)	180°
4 (quadrilateral)	360°
5 (pentagon)	540°

You can calculate the angle sum using any of these formulae.
n is the number of sides and S is the angle sum.

$S = (n - 2) \times 180°$

$S = (180n - 360)°$

$S = (2n - 4)$ right angles

Test yourself

1 What is the angle sum of:

a) an octagon

b) a dodecagon?

2 Find the angles marked with letters.

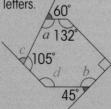

3 Find the number of sides of these polygons, if the angle sum is:

a) 900°

b) 1440°

c) 2340°

Check the facts

Regular polygons have these properties:
• **All the angles are equal** • **All the sides are the same length.**

Note: you **can** have one without the other! Neither of these polygons is regular:

Sides all the same but angles vary   Angles equal but sides vary

Number of sides	Interior angle	Exterior angle
3 (equilateral triangle)	60°	120°
4 (square)	90°	90°
5 (regular pentagon)	108°	72°
6 (regular hexagon)	120°	60°

You can work out the interior angles for other regular polygons in two ways:

1 Work out the angle sum, then divide by the number of sides.

2 Divide 360° by the number of sides to find one exterior angle. Take this away from 180°.

Test yourself

1 Use method 1 to find one interior angle of each of these regular polygons.

a)   b)   c)

2 Use method 2 to find one interior angle if a regular polygon has:
a) 12 sides   b) 15 sides   c) 20 sides

3 Fill in the missing angles, then find the number of sides for each regular polygon.

Interior angle	Exterior angle	Number of sides
	40°	
170°		
165°		
	22.5°	

Shape and space

BBC GCSE Check and Test: Maths

Check the facts

> **A tessellation is a regular pattern of shapes that covers a plane completely, without any gaps.**

You can only ever draw part of a tessellation because tessellations are infinitely large. Here are some examples of tessellations that only use one type of shape:

 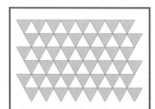

> **Polygons will only fit together round a vertex if all the interior angles add up to 360°.**

Tessellations are also possible in three dimensions. A solid tessellation is an arrangement of 3D shapes that fills space completely.

Test yourself

1 Can you make a tessellation from these shapes?
Give reasons for your answers. Sketch those that are possible.

a) regular hexagons   b) regular pentagons

c) parallelograms   d) rectangles

e) isosceles triangles   f) regular octagons

g) kites   h) pentagons with one line of symmetry

2 By adding up interior angles, find combinations of regular polygons that will 'fill up' 360° at a point. Investigate how a tessellation made from these shapes will look. Are there any that don't work?

Shape and space

www.bbc.co.uk/revision

Check the facts

Parts of a circle

Shape and space

h

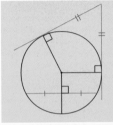

The two tangents from any point to a circle are perpendicular to the radii at the point of contact. They are also equal in length. If a chord and radius are perpendicular, the radius bisects the chord.

Four points on the circumference form a **cyclic quadrilateral**.
$a + c = b + d = 180°$

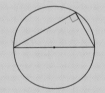

A triangle made from a diameter and a point on the circumference has a right angle opposite the diameter.

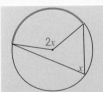

The angle subtended at the centre by an arc is double the angle subtended at a point on the circumference.

Test yourself

1 Calculate angles p and q.

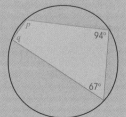

2 Find x and thus all the angles in degrees.

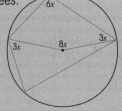

BBC GCSE Check and Test: Maths

Shape and space

Check the facts

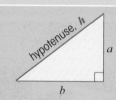

In any right-angled
triangle, the hypotenuse
is the side opposite
the right angle.

Pythagoras' theorem states that this relationship is true in any right-angled triangle: $a^2 + b^2 = h^2$.

So to calculate the hypotenuse, use $h = \sqrt{a^2 + b^2}$

To calculate one of the other sides, use $a = \sqrt{h^2 - b^2}$ or $b = \sqrt{h^2 - a^2}$
(it doesn't matter which side is called a and which is called b).

You can also use Pythagoras' theorem to
calculate the diagonal of a rectangle:

or to find the distance between two points
on a co-ordinate grid.

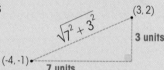

Test yourself

Round answers to 3 significant figures where necessary.

1 Find the unmarked side in each triangle.

a)

12 cm · 5 cm

b)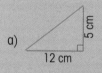

7 cm · 28 cm

c)

3 m · 3.125 m

d)

60 cm · 131 cm

2 Calculate the diagonal or side of each rectangle.

a)

12 m · 9 m

b)

60 km · 65 km

3 Calculate the distance between each pair of points.
   a) (1, 2) and (6, 4)   b) (3, 0) and (5, −2)
   c) (18, −12) and (42, −5)   d) (2.5, 0.8) and (0.8, 2.5)

Check the facts

Two shapes that are identical are congruent.

If the following features of two triangles match, the triangles are congruent.

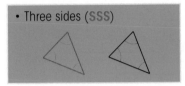

- Three sides (SSS)

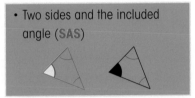

- Two sides and the included angle (SAS)

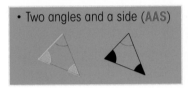

- Two angles and a side (AAS)

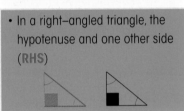

- In a right–angled triangle, the hypotenuse and one other side (RHS)

Shapes that are the same apart from their size are similar.

Similar shapes are **enlargements** of each other. Two triangles are similar if they have identical angles. Their sides are automatically in the same **ratio**.

Test yourself

1 Identify whether the shapes in each pair are similar, congruent or neither.

a)
4 cm
75°
6.5 cm

4 cm
75°
6.5 cm

b)
12 cm
8 cm
18 cm

18 mm
12 mm
27 mm

2 The shapes in each group are similar. Use this to find the unknown lengths and angles.

a)
20 m
8 m

x
13 m

b)
x
8 cm
6 cm

15 cm
9 cm
y

Shape and space

BBC GCSE Check and Test: Maths

Check the facts

In a right-angled triangle, the sides are given temporary 'names' according to where they are in relation to a chosen angle x.

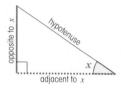 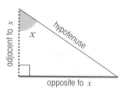

In similar triangles, the three sides are always in the same ratio. These trigonometric ratios ('trig.' ratios) have names.

• The **sine** of an angle is $= \dfrac{\text{opposite side}}{\text{hypotenuse}} = \sin x.$

So **opp** = hyp × sin x and **hyp** = $\dfrac{\text{opp}}{\sin x}$.

• The **cosine** of an angle is $= \dfrac{\text{adjacent side}}{\text{hypotenuse}} = \cos x.$

So **adj** = hyp × cos x and **hyp** = $\dfrac{\text{adj}}{\cos x}$.

• The **tangent** of an angle is $\dfrac{\text{opposite side}}{\text{adjacent side}} = \tan x.$

So **opp** = adj × tan x and **adj** = $\dfrac{\text{opp}}{\tan x}$.

> Use the 'words' **SOH–CAH–TOA** (**Sin = Opp/Hyp, Cos=Adj/Hyp, Tan = Opp/Adj**) to remember these rules.

Test yourself

For each triangle, decide which ratio is needed and find the side marked with letters. Round answers to 3 s.f. where necessary.

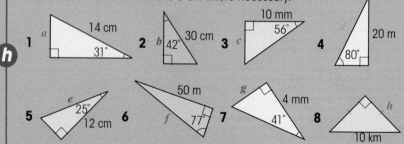

Shape and space

Check the facts

If you know the sides in a right–angled triangle and need to work out an angle, you can calculate the trig. ratio, then use this to find the angle. The **inverse trig. functions** on your calculator are designed for this task. They may be marked sin⁻¹ cos⁻¹ tan⁻¹, arcsin arccos arctan or asn acs atn.

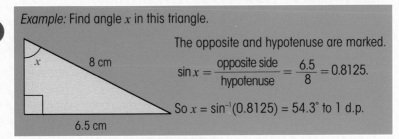

Example: Find angle x in this triangle.

The opposite and hypotenuse are marked.

$$\sin x = \frac{\text{opposite side}}{\text{hypotenuse}} = \frac{6.5}{8} = 0.8125.$$

So $x = \sin^{-1}(0.8125) = 54.3°$ to 1 d.p.

8 cm

6.5 cm

h

Test yourself

Work out the lettered angles using the correct inverse functions.
Give answers to 1 d.p. where necessary.

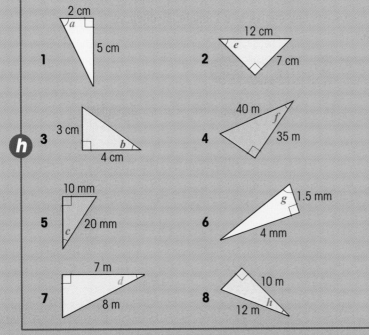

1 2 cm, a, 5 cm

2 12 cm, e, 7 cm

3 3 cm, b, 4 cm

4 40 m, f, 35 m

5 10 mm, c, 20 mm

6 g, 1.5 mm, 4 mm

7 7 m, d, 8 m

8 10 m, h, 12 m

h

BBC GCSE Check and Test: Maths

Trigonometry: the sine and the cosine rules

Check the facts

In any triangle, whatever angles, these two important rules apply.
Using these names for the sides and angles…

Shape and space

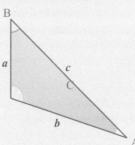

h

The sine rule: $\dfrac{a}{\sin A} = \dfrac{b}{\sin B} = \dfrac{c}{\sin C}$.

The cosine rule: $a^2 = b^2 + c^2 - 2bc\cos A$
(also $b^2 = a^2 + c^2 - 2ac\cos B$ and $c^2 = a^2 + c^2 - 2ab\cos C$).

**Finding all the sides and angles in a triangle is called solving
the triangle.**

Test yourself

Find the lettered sides and angles using the sine and cosine rules.

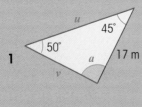

1

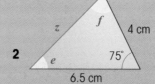

2

h

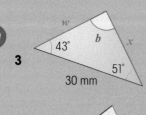

3

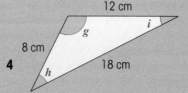

4

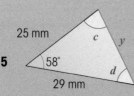

5

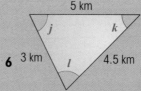

6

Check the facts

Mathematical transformations start with an original point or shape (the object) and transform it (into the image).

A **translation** is a 'sliding' movement. When an object is translated, the image is the same size and has not rotated at all. To describe a translation completely, you need to give the movements in the x and y directions as a **column vector**. Column vectors have two **components**, like co–ordinates, but are written differently because they show movement, not position.

To translate a point, add the components of the vector to the co-ordinates of the point.

Example: Translate the triangle (1, 8), (5, 8), (1, 6) using the vector $\begin{pmatrix} 5 \\ -4 \end{pmatrix}$.

Working: For example, (1, 8) translates to (6, 4) because $1 + 5 = 6$ and $8 + (-4) = 4$.

Answer:

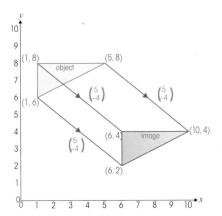

Test yourself

Draw a co–ordinate grid with x and y from –10 to 10. Use the given vectors to translate points. The object for each part is the image from the last part. Write down the coordinates of each image.

1 Object point: (4, 1). Vector: $\begin{pmatrix} 5 \\ 4 \end{pmatrix}$.

2 $\begin{pmatrix} -2 \\ -5 \end{pmatrix}$ **3** $\begin{pmatrix} 2 \\ -7 \end{pmatrix}$ **4** $\begin{pmatrix} -5 \\ 8 \end{pmatrix}$ **5** $\begin{pmatrix} -2 \\ -7 \end{pmatrix}$

6 $\begin{pmatrix} -8 \\ 3 \end{pmatrix}$ **7** $\begin{pmatrix} -2 \\ 4 \end{pmatrix}$ **8** $\begin{pmatrix} 2 \\ 3 \end{pmatrix}$ **9** $\begin{pmatrix} 8 \\ 2 \end{pmatrix}$

10 $\begin{pmatrix} 2 \\ -5 \end{pmatrix}$ (You should be back at the start.)

Check the facts

In a rotation, an object is turned by a given angle about a fixed point called the centre of rotation. The centre is the only point left unchanged by the rotation.

This shows 90°, 180° and 270° anticlockwise rotations about the centre (5, 5).

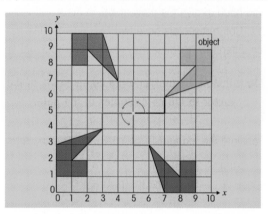

Given a rotation, you can usually find the centre by trial and error, using a piece of tracing paper. Trace the object, then fix different points for rotation until the image is in the right place.

To find the centre of rotation by construction, follow these steps:

h

- Join two pairs of corresponding points on the object and image.

- Construct the perpendicular bisectors of these lines.

- The centre of rotation is the point of intersection of the bisectors.

Test yourself

Draw a co-ordinate grid with $-10 \leqslant x, y \leqslant 10$.

Draw an object shape by joining these coordinates:
$(1, 1) \rightarrow (4, 1) \rightarrow (2, 3) \rightarrow (2, 2) \rightarrow (1, 2) \rightarrow (1, 1)$.

Rotate the object as follows. All the answers fit onto one diagram.

1	90°	(4, 1)		

1 90° (4, 1)   **2** 90° (1, 2)

3 180° (1, 1)   **4** 180° (4, 3)

5 90° (−1, 4)   **6** 180° (−2, 4)

7 90° (5, −4)   **8** 180° (−3, −3)

9 90° (−1, −5)   **10** 90° (9, 1)

Shape and space

Check the facts

When an object is reflected, the object and image make a symmetrical pattern. The mirror line used for the reflection is the line of symmetry. Reflection in any line is possible, but the most likely ones you will be asked to use are these:

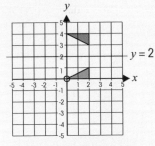

Lines parallel to the x-axis

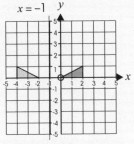

Lines parallel to the y-axis

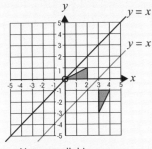
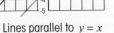

Lines parallel to $y = x$

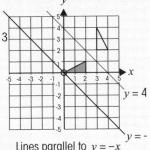
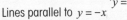

Lines parallel to $y = -x$

Test yourself

1 Draw a co–ordinate grid with $-10 \leqslant x, y \leqslant 10$.

Draw an object shape by joining these coordinates:

$(2, 0) \rightarrow (5, 0) \rightarrow (5, 2) \rightarrow (4, 2) \rightarrow (4, 1) \rightarrow (2, 1) \rightarrow (2, 0)$.

Reflect the object in the following lines. All the answers fit onto one diagram.

a) $x = 5$

b) $y = 4$

c) $y = -2$

d) $y = x - 5$

e) $y = 9 - x$

f) $x = -2$

g) $y = x + 4$

h) $y = -x - 4$

Shape and space

BBC GCSE Check and Test: Maths

Check the facts

> **To describe an enlargement you need to give a**
> scale factor **and a** centre of enlargement.

The scale factor affects the size of the image. The centre of enlargement affects the **position** of the image.

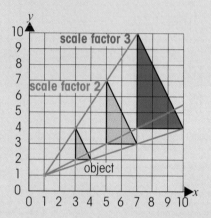

To find the centre of enlargement, draw lines through corresponding points on the object and image. These all intersect at the centre of enlargement. To find the scale factor, divide the length of a line on the image by the corresponding line on the object.

Test yourself

Draw a co-ordinate grid with $-10 \leqslant x, y \leqslant 10$.
Draw an object shape by joining these coordinates:
$(-4, 4) \rightarrow (-1, 4) \rightarrow (-1, 1) \rightarrow (-2, 1) \rightarrow (-2, 2) \rightarrow (-3, 3) \rightarrow (-4, 3) \rightarrow (-4, 4)$.
Carry out these enlargements. The answers will all fit on the same grid.

1 Centre $(0, 0)$, scale factor 2.

2 Centre $(0, 0)$, scale factor -1.

3 Centre $(0, 0)$, scale factor -2.5.

4 Centre $(2, 6)$, scale factor 3.

5 Centre $(-5, 2)$, scale factor 0.5.

6 Centre $(0, 4)$, scale factor -2.

Check the facts

To construct a right angle at a given point on a line (also called erecting a perpendicular):

Mark the point where you want to construct the right angle.

Make marks on the line either side of the point, using the same raduis.

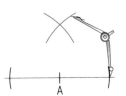

Increase the radius by about half. Using the last two marks as centres, draw two arcs as shown.

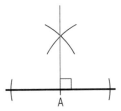

Join the original point to the point of intersection of the two arcs. This makes the right angle.

To construct a 60° angle at a point:

Mark the vertex of the angle.

Using any radius, make a mark on the line.

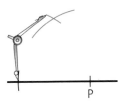

Using both marks on the line as centres, keeping the same radius, draw two crossing arcs as shown.

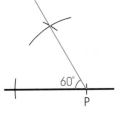

Join the vertex to the point of intersection of the two arcs. This makes the 60° angle.

Test yourself

1 Practise the constructions above. Check your accuracy with a protractor.

Shape and space

BBC GCSE Check and Test: Maths

Check the facts

To construct the perpendicular bisector of two points:

Using the same radius and the points as centres, draw two arcs on either side of the line joining the points.

The line joining the points of intersection of the arcs is the perpendicular bisector of the two points.

You can use this construction to bisect any line.

To bisect an angle:

Using the vertex of the angle as centre and keeping the radius the same, make a mark on each arm.

Keep the same radius. Using the last two marks as centres, draw two crossing arcs as shown.

Join the vertex to the point of intersection of the two arcs. This line bisects the original angle.

Test yourself

Check all of your constructions with ruler and protractor.

1 a) Mark two points 10 cm apart. Construct their perpendicular bisector.
b) Draw a line 7.6 cm long. Bisect it.

2 Draw the following angles using a protractor, then bisect them.
a) 74°   b) 28°   c) 44°

3 By combining the constructions in this section with those from the last section, draw angles of
a) 45°   b) 30°

4 Use the perpendicular bisector construction to draw a rhombus with sides 5 cm long and one diagonal of 6 cm.

Check the facts

A set of positions generated by a rule is called a **locus**. The four major types are as follows:

A fixed distance from a fixed point: a circle.

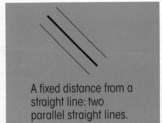

A fixed distance from a straight line: two parallel straight lines.

Equidistant from two fixed points: the perpendicular bisector of the points.

Equidistant from two straight lines: the bisectors of the angles between the lines.

Sometimes you need to combine the first two types:

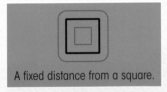

A fixed distance from a square.

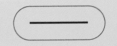

A fixed distance from a line segment.

Test yourself

1 Mercury is 58 000 000 km from the sun.
Venus is 108 000 000 km from the sun.
Earth's distance is 149 000 000 km.
Using a scale of 1 cm = 20 000 000 km, draw a diagram showing the loci of these planets.

2 a) Construct an equilateral triangle with sides of 10 cm.
  b) Draw the locus of points that are 4 cm from the triangle.
  c) Pick any two vertices of your triangle. Draw the locus of points that are equidistant from these two vertices.

3 a) Construct a triangle ABC with sides AB = 10 cm, AC = 8 cm and BC = 6 cm.
  b) Draw the locus of points that are equidistant from AB and AC.
  c) The locus intersects BC at P. Measure PB.

Shape and space

BBC GCSE Check and Test: Maths

Check the facts

Often you need to combine information from two or more loci to solve a problem. Sometimes this will lead to a region or area, sometimes to a line segment, sometimes to one or more points.

Example:

Find the co-ordinates of all points that are 4 units from the point (5, 4) and equidistant from the lines $y = x$ and $y = 6$.

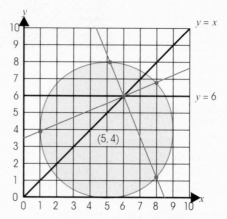

The loci intersect at four points. To 1 d.p., the co-ordinates are (5.2, 8.0), (7.8, 6.8), (7.9, 1.3) and (1.0, 3.9).

Test yourself

1 a) Draw a co-ordinate grid with $0 \leqslant x, y \leqslant 10$.
Draw a rectangle whose sides are parallel to the axes and whose opposite corners are (2, 8) and (8, 3).

b) Draw the locus of points that are 1 unit from the rectangle.

c) Draw the locus of points that are 8 units from the point (10, 1).

d) What are the co-ordinates of points that lie on both loci?

2 Three radio transmitters form an equilateral triangle ABC with sides of 100 km. The range of the transmitter at A is 70 km, at B 60 km and at C 50 km. Using a scale of 1 cm to 10 km, construct a scale diagram to show the region where signals from all 3 transmitters can be received.

Check the facts

Conversion graphs are used to convert between two amounts that are linked (usually by a mathematical rule). These could be measurement units, currencies, costs of goods or services, etc.

Examples of conversion graphs:

Test yourself

1 This graph compares the quarterly mobile phone charges from two different companies.

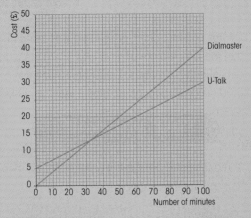

a) On Dialmaster, how much do you pay for i) 25 minutes of calls; ii) 1 hour?

b) On U-Talk, how much do you pay for i) half an hour; (ii) 90 minutes?

c) On Dialmaster, how many minutes do you get for i) £20; (ii) £34?

d) On U-Talk, how many minutes do you get for i) £10; (ii) £26?

e) If you didn't use your phone much, which company is cheaper?

f) Over what number of minutes does the other company become cheaper?

2 Draw a graph to convert up to £50 to US dollars. The exchange rate is £1 = $1.40.

Use your graph to calculate the amount of British currency equivalent to $50.

Graphs

BBC GCSE Check and Test: Maths

Graphs

Check the facts

Graphs of this type show the way something changes with time. Examples are a patient's temperature chart, the electrical power used by a household during a day and the amount of water in a reservoir during a year.

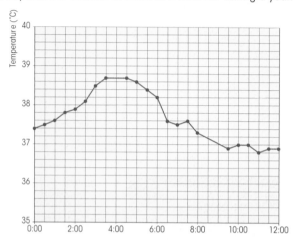

On this patient's chart, no reading was taken at 4:00. It's safe to assume that the temperature at 4:00 was 38.7°C, though it may have been higher. Similarly, the line gives a reasonable estimate of the temperature between 8:00 and 9:30, though no actual readings exist.

Test yourself

1 The temperature of a hot water system is measured and recorded. These are the results.

Time	2200	2300	0000	0300	0400	0430	0500	0530	0600	0700	0800
Temperature (°C)	21	19	18	13	12	19	27	34	38	36	23

a) Plot a graph of temperature against time.
b) Estimate the temperature at 0100 and 0200.
c) Estimate the times when the temperature was 30°C.

2 These are the share prices of a company over the course of a year.

Date	Jan 1	Mar 1	May 1	Sep 1	Nov 1	Dec 1	Jan 1
Price (pence)	35.3	41.8	46.5	58.7	53.2	51.0	46.6

a) Plot a graph of share price against date.
b) Estimate the share price on Feb 1, Jul 1 and Dec 15.
c) Estimate the dates when the shares cost 50p.

Check the facts

Journeys can be documented by travel graphs.

Here is the same journey plotted as distance against time and as speed against time:

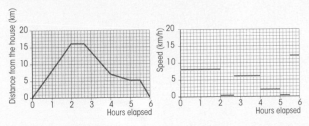

Notice that in reality there wouldn't be any sharp points or jumps. These graphs are only rough approximations. The gradient of a line on a distance-time graph represents the speed over that time interval.

 Note that constant acceleration or deceleration is shown on a distance-time graph as a curve (the gradient of the curve at any point represents speed), and on a speed-time graph as a straight line. The area under a speed-time graph represents the distance travelled.

Test yourself

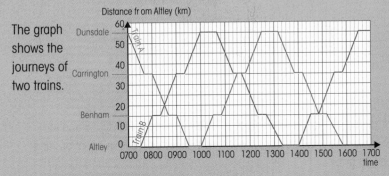

The graph shows the journeys of two trains.

1 What time does train A arrive in Carrington?

2 How long does train B wait at Benham?

3 How far is it from Benham to Dunsdale?

4 At what time do the trains first pass each other?

5 Once during the day, both trains wait together at the same station. Which station, and for how long?

6 What happens at 1450?

7 What is the average speed of train A between Benham and Carrington?

8 Draw up the timetable for this service.

Graphs

Check the facts

This section is about plotting graphs from equations or functions. Here are some common ones:

$$y = 2x + 1 \qquad y = x^2 \qquad y = x^3 \qquad y = \frac{1}{x} \qquad y = \sin x$$

To plot a graph, you need a table of values that you construct from the equation.

For example, to draw a graph of $y = 10 - x^2$, pick a range of values for x and calculate the corresponding values of y:

x	-4	-3	-2	-1	0	1	2	3	4
x^2	16	9	4	1	0	1	4	9	16
$y = 10 - x^2$	-6	1	6	9	10	9	6	1	-6

Draw axes and plot the points:

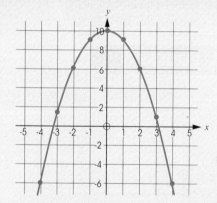

Note that all graphs of the form $y = mx + c$, where m and c stand for fixed numbers, are straight lines. Almost all other types of equation have curved graphs.

Test yourself

Plot the following graphs. Decide on suitable scales for each one.

1 $y = 2x - 3$ 2 $y = 5 - x$ 3 $y = 1 + \frac{1}{2}x$

4 $y = x^2 - 4$ 5 $y = \frac{1}{2}x^2$ 6 $y = x^2 - 2x + 1$

7 $y = 2^x$ 8 $y = \sqrt{x}$ 9 $y = \cos x°$

10 $y = \dfrac{x + 3}{x - 2}$

h

Check the facts

There are three basic types of straight-line graphs.

Lines parallel to the x-axis have equations of the form $y = a$, where a is a constant. Lines parallel to the y-axis have equations of the form $x = b$, where b is a constant.

In the general equation for straight-line graphs, $y = mx + c$, m represents the gradient and c the y-intercept.

So the graph crosses the y-axis at c and $\dfrac{\text{increase in } y}{\text{increase in } x} = m$

Lines with the same gradient are parallel.

 In the case of a curved graph, the gradient of the curve at any point is equal to the gradient of the tangent at that point.

Test yourself

1 Write down the gradient and y-intercept of these graphs.

a) $y = 2x + 3$ b) $y = 4x - 6$

c) $y = -3x + 1$ d) $y = x + 5$

e) $y = 2x$ f) $y = 1 - 5x$

g) $y = 25 - x$ h) $y = \dfrac{x}{2} + 1$

i) $y = \dfrac{5x}{4}$ j) $y = \dfrac{2(x - 6)}{3}$

2 Find the equations of these graphs.

a) 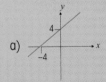 b) c)

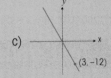 (3, –12)

d) 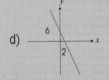 e) f)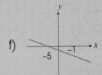

g) 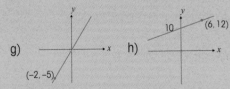 h)

(–2, –5)

(6, 12)

Check the facts

Every straight line divides the co-ordinate plane into two regions. These regions can be described using inequalities.

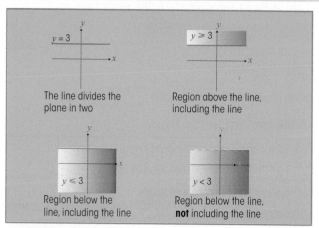

The line divides the plane in two

Region above the line, including the line

Region below the line, including the line

Region below the line, **not** including the line

The same rules apply for sloping lines.

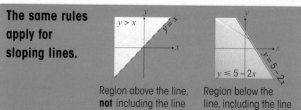

Region above the line, **not** including the line

Region below the line, including the line

The only exception is for regions to the right or left of vertical lines.

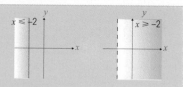

Combinations of regions can be used to enclose areas.

Test yourself

1 Shade areas to illustrate these inequalities.

a) $y \geqslant 1$ b) $y > 2$ c) $x < 5$ d) $x \leqslant -1$
e) $y \geqslant -x$ f) $y < 2x$ g) $y \leqslant 4 - x$ h) $y \leqslant \frac{1}{2}x + 1$
i) $x < y$ j) $y \geqslant x^2$

2 Find the area, in square units, of these shapes:
   a) The rectangle described by $x \geqslant -3, x \leqslant 5, y \geqslant 2, y \leqslant 6$
   (this can also be written $-3 \leqslant x \leqslant 5, 2 \leqslant y \leqslant 6$).
   b) The triangle described by $y \geqslant -4, y \leqslant 2x, y \leqslant 6 - x$.

Check the facts

A bar chart represents the frequency of an item in a
sample by the height of a bar. Data items that are not
numerical, or which are discrete, can be represented
like this, with the bars separated or not.

In a **pictogram**, the bars are replaced by pictures. Each picture represents a
fixed number of data items.

Numerical data that is **continuous**, such as sizes, masses or times, **must**
have joined bars.

Comparative bar charts can be made by placing two or more sets of data
side-by-side, or by stacking them.

h A **histogram** is a form of bar chart in which the area of each bar
represents the frequency. This makes it possible to represent data with
unequal class widths.

Test yourself

Answer the questions using this bar chart.

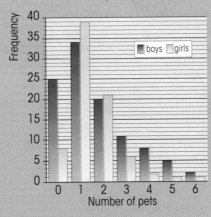

Pets owned by sixth form students

1 Produce a table containing the data from the bar chart.

a Calculate the total number of students for each number of pets.

b How many students took part in the survey?

c How many pets did they have between them?

d What was the average number of pets per student?

Handling data

BBC GCSE Check and Test: Maths

Check the facts

A pie chart is useful for comparing fractions of a whole.

When drawing a pie chart, calculate how many degrees are needed to represent one item, then calculate the numbers of degrees for each sector. Check that these total 360°.

Example: A group of people were asked what they had for breakfast. Display these results on a pie chart.

Breakfast	Toast	Cereals	Cooked	Drink only
Frequency	14	11	3	2

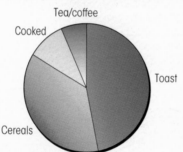

Breakfast preferences of 30 people

The total is 30 people, so each person needs 360° ÷ 30 = 12° on the pie chart.
The angles will be
14 × 12° = **168°**,
11 × 12° = **132°**,
3 × 12° = **36°**,
2 × 12° = **24°**.

When reading a pie chart, you may need to measure angles or you may need to estimate fractions.

Test yourself

1 Spencer runs a plant nursery. This is how he splits up the planting beds.

Type of plant	Flowers	Vegetables	Fruit Trees
Number of beds	20	11	14

Draw a pie chart to illustrate the information.

2 Furniture World employ these people:

Job title	Managers	Sales Assistants	Warehouse Workers	Drivers
Number of People	10	68	52	14

Draw a pie chart to illustrate the information.

Check the facts

Scatter diagrams **are used to test if there is a link between two sets of data.**

For example, your height and armspan are supposed to be very similar. A sample of 100 people produced this scatter diagram. Each point represents one person.

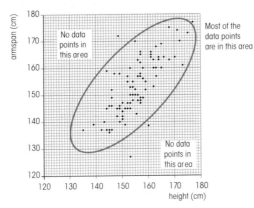

As height goes up, so does armspan. They are **positively correlated**.

Test yourself

In each question, plot the scatter diagram on graph paper. Identify the type of correlation.

1 A group of students' exam marks were compared.

Year 10 (%)	65	32	40	58	48	50	60	68	54	81
Mock GCSE (%)	67	45	38	55	55	57	49	56	50	75
Year 10 (%)	44	59	62	75	72	17	85	30	50	43
Mock GCSE (%)	60	60	54	69	72	25	88	42	56	52
Year 10 (%)	47	52	34	56	56	70	55	61	77	60
Mock GCSE (%)	56	69	40	58	48	75	58	57	74	70

2 Weather data for each month.

Month	Jan	Feb	Mar	Apr	May	Jun	Jul	Aug	Sep	Oct	Nov	Dec
mm rainfall	83	72	90	51	18	53	7	0	24	25	55	63
hrs sunshine	36	25	50	62	95	88	91	97	84	75	67	45

Note: *keep your scatter diagrams for use later.*

Handling data

BBC GCSE Check and Test: Maths

95

Check the facts

**Often, a line of best fit is added to a scatter diagram.
This has two uses: • to show the correlation more clearly;
• to make predictions about other data items.**

The line has to 'follow the trend' of the data points. This is quite easy to do 'by eye'.

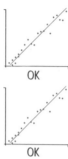

OK

Too steep

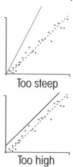

Not steep enough

OK

Too high

Too low

To make predictions using the line, simply read from one scale to the other as on any graph. Note that the line is only useful for this purpose **within the range of the data** or slightly outside it.

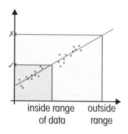

inside range of data   outside range

 Calculate the means of both sets of data values. Mark a 'mean point' on the scatter diagram. The line of best fit must pass through this point.

Test yourself

The question numbers match the scatter diagrams from the last question section. Mark the lines of best fit on your scatter diagrams and use them to answer the questions.

1 a) Estimate the Mock mark for someone who scored 25% in the Year 10 exam.

   b) Estimate the Year 10 exam mark for someone who scored 63% in the Mock.

2 a) The following year, there was a month with 55 hours of sunshine. Estimate the rainfall for that month.

   b) Estimate the hours of sunshine for a month with 30 mm rainfall.

 Calculate the mean points and make sure the lines pass through them.

Check the facts

Averages are used in statistics to give the idea of a 'typical' value for a set of data. There are three main types of average: the mode, median and mean.

The **mode** is the most common value. In the case of data in groups or classes, the group with the highest frequency is called the **modal** group or class.

There may be more than one mode if there's a 'tie for first place'. It's the only average that exists for non-numerical data.

Example: Find the mode of this set of numbers: 2, 3, 1, 6, 2, 1, 3, 3, 4, 2. There are three 2s and three 3s, so 2 and 3 are the modes.

The **median** is the middle value in a set, when all the numbers are arranged in order. If you have an even number of data items, the median is halfway between the two in the middle. The median for grouped data has to be estimated in a different way (see sections 95 and 96). There is only one median for any set of data.

Example: Find the median of this set of numbers: 2, 3, 1, 6, 2, 1, 3, 3, 4, 2. Arrange the numbers in order: 1, 1, 2, 2, 2, 3, 3, 3, 4, 6. The median is halfway between the fifth and sixth positions, which are a 2 and a 3. So the median is 2.5.

Test yourself

1 Find the mode and median for each data set.
   a) 4, 0, 1, 0, 3, 0, 2, 1, 2
   b) 11, 11.5, 11.3, 11.4, 11.5, 11.2, 11.3, 11.4, 11.5, 11.4
   c) −2, −3, 0, 1, −4, 5, 8
   d) 304, 301, 298, 297, 300, 302, 299, 289

2 The following data shows the speed v of 50 tennis serves in km/h.

123	176	120	137	139	121	124	121	155	147
188	134	126	179	197	153	129	151	169	122
141	130	124	139	177	190	123	179	122	169
193	151	122	121	120	189	146	143	193	176
167	126	190	172	133	130	127	144	187	149

   a) Tally the data into classes $120 \leqslant v \leqslant 130$, $130 \leqslant v \leqslant 140$, $140 \leqslant v \leqslant 150$, etc.
   b) Determine the modal speed class.
   c) Which class contains the median speed?

Handling data

BBC GCSE Check and Test: Maths

Handling data

Check the facts

> The **mean** is the most frequently used average.
> It is calculated by taking the sum of all the data items,
> then dividing by the number of items.

Example: Find the mean of this set of numbers:
2, 3, 1, 6, 2, 1, 3, 3, 4, 2.

The total is 27. There are ten numbers, so the mean is $27 \div 10 = 2.7$.

In a frequency table, multiply the data values by the frequencies.

Example: Find the mean shoe size.

Shoe size	Frequency	Product
6	35	$6 \times 35 = 210$
7	57	$7 \times 57 = 399$
8	28	$8 \times 28 = 224$
Total	120	833

Mean = $833 \div 120 = 6.94$ to 2 d.p.

The mean for grouped data has to be estimated in a different way
(see section 94).

The **range** is not an average, but tells you how 'spread out' the data is. It is
simply the difference between the smallest and largest data items.

Test yourself

1 Calculate the mean and range of each data set. Round the mean to a
sensible accuracy if necessary.
a) 4, 0, 1, 0, 3, 0, 2, 1, 2
b) 11, 11.5, 11.3, 11.4, 11.5, 11.2, 11.3, 11.4, 11.5, 11.4
c) −2, −3, 0, 1, −4, 5, 8
d) 304, 301, 298, 297, 300, 302, 299, 289

2 Calculate the mean length of surname from this sample.

Letters in surname	3	4	5	6	7	8	9	10	11
Frequency	9	61	202	262	219	125	67	44	11

3 a) Write 2 numbers with mean = 10 and range = 4.
b) Write 2 numbers with mean = 10 and range = 10.
c) Write 3 numbers with mean = 10 and range = 6.

Check the facts

Finding the mean of a set of data depends on knowing the total of all the data items. When data is in groups, however, this is impossible. You need to estimate the total. To do this, you **use mid-interval values (MIVs)**. This means assuming that all the items in a group are exactly in the middle of the group.

Example: Estimate the mean age of these customers, to the nearest month.

The MIV for the first group is exactly halfway between the minimum and maximum ages for the group: $(18 + 21) \div 2 = 19.5$. The **product** column contains an estimate for the total from each group.

Age	Frequency	MIV	Product (frequency × MIV)
18-21	1344	19.5	26 208
22-25	3650	23.5	85 775
26-30	4825	28	135 100
31-40	3240	35.5	115 020
41-50	2721	45.5	123 805.5
51-60	1820	55.5	101 010
61-80	1032	70.5	72 756
81-100	320	90.5	28 960
Total	18 952		688 634.5

Estimated mean = 688 634.5 ÷ 18 952 = 36.335…years
= 36 years 4 months to the nearest month.

Test yourself

Estimate the mean of each data set.

1 This table shows the parking times for cars in a multi-storey car park.

Parking time (min)	5-30	26-60	61-120	121-180	181-300
Number of cars	78	125	540	154	26

2 This table shows mock GCSE marks obtained by a set of Year 11 pupils.

Mark	20-40	41-50	51-60	61-70
Frequency	2	8	19	48
Mark	71-80	81-90	91-100	101-120
Frequency	73	25	12	6

Handling data

BBC GCSE Check and Test: Maths

Check the facts

A grouped set of data can be plotted on a cumulative frequency diagram.

Example: These tables show the exam marks of 200 Year 10 students.

Mark	Frequency
0-20	1
21-30	7
31-40	22
41-50	50
51-60	75
61-70	27
71-80	12
81-100	6

Mark	Cumulative frequency
≤20	1
≤30	8
≤40	30
≤50	80
≤60	155
≤70	182
≤80	194
≤100	200

Plot the cumulative frequency against the mark.

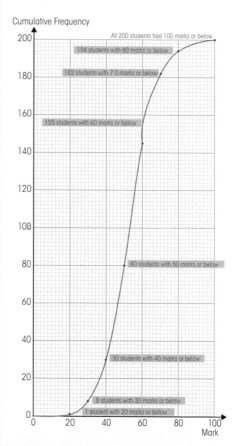

All 200 students had 100 marks or below
194 students with 80 marks or below
182 students with 70 marks or below
155 students with 60 marks or below
80 students with 50 marks or below
30 students with 40 marks or below
8 students with 30 marks or below
1 student with 20 marks or below

Handling data

Test yourself

Use the data sets from 'Test yourself' in section 94.

Draw a cumulative frequency curve for each one. Keep the graphs for 'Test yourself' in section 96.

Handling data

Check the facts

With a cumulative frequency diagram, it is possible to estimate the median of a set of grouped data. You can also generate another useful statistic, the interquartile range.

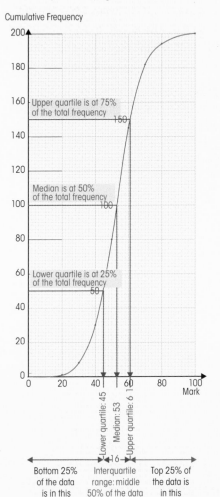

Cumulative Frequency

Upper quartile is at 75% of the total frequency

Median is at 50% of the total frequency

Lower quartile is at 25% of the total frequency

Mark

Lower quartile: 45

Median: 53

Upper quartile: 6 1

Bottom 25% of the data is in this range

Interquartile range: middle 50% of the data

Top 25% of the data is in this range

- The **median** splits the data into two halves, the lower 50% and the upper 50%.

- The **median and quartiles** divide the data into four quarters.

- The **interquartile range** contains the middle two quarters, 50% of the data. This can be more useful to analyse how 'spread out' the data is, as the full range might contain extreme values.

Test yourself

Use the cumulative frequency curves from 'Test yourself' in section 95.

Estimate the median and interquartile range for each one.

Check the facts

Things that happen according to the laws of chance are called **events**. Events have **outcomes**. Each outcome of a chance event has a **probability**, a number between 0 and 1 that describes how likely it is. A probability of 0 means an outcome is **impossible**: 1 means it is **certain**.

Example: the event of flipping a fair coin has two outcomes, head and tail, with equal probabilities. This is expressed as $P(\text{head}) = P(\text{tail}) = \frac{1}{2}$. These outcomes are called **exclusive** because they can't both happen at once. When outcomes are exclusive, their probabilities must add up to 1.

Theoretical probability is calculated by analysing a situation mathematically. The probability can be used to predict the expected frequency of the outcomes of a number of **trials**.

Example: On this spinner the probabilities are

$P(\text{white}) = \frac{1}{4}$ and $P(\text{orange}) = \frac{3}{4}$ by looking at the angles for each sector. If this spinner spun 100 times, you would expect about $\frac{1}{4}$ of the spins, 25, to land on white.

Experimental probability is determined by analysing the results of a number of trials of the event.

Example: A drawing pin is flipped and lands on its point 42 times out of 100 trials. The experimental probability is $P(\text{point down}) = 42 \div 100 = 0.42$.

Test yourself

1 Using a standard pack of playing cards, well shuffled, what is the probability of picking:
a) A club
b) An ace
c) A Jack, Queen or King
d) A red card

2 Each day in a biscuit factory, 50 packets of cream crackers were randomly tested. These were the results:

Broken biscuits per pkt	Mon	Tue	Wed	Thu	Fri
0	33	37	39	30	35
1	14	10	9	13	4
2	3	2	2	5	1
3	0	1	0	2	0

Calculate the probability that a packet will contain:
a) no broken biscuits; b) some broken biscuits; c) one broken biscuit.

Check the facts

When two events are **independent** (i.e. the outcome of one has no effect on the outcome of the other), it is possible to calculate the combined probabilities for both events. When all the outcomes are equally likely, a list or table is all that is needed to list all the possible results.

Sometimes an organised list will do: if three coins are flipped, what is the probability that they will all show the same face (i.e. 3 heads or 3 tails)? The outcomes are HHH, HHT, HTH, HTT, THH, THT, TTH, TTT. There are 8 possible outcomes, of which 2 show the same face. So $P(3 \text{ the same}) = \frac{2}{8} = \frac{1}{4}$.

In more complicated situations, a table called a **possibility space diagram** is useful. To work out the probability of scoring a total of 8 with two dice, put the results into a table like this one.

1ˢᵗ die

	1	2	3	4	5	6
1	2	3	4	5	6	7
2	3	4	5	6	7	8
3	4	5	6	7	8	9
4	5	6	7	8	9	10
5	6	7	8	9	10	11
6	7	8	9	10	11	12

2ⁿᵈ die

So $P(8) = \frac{5}{36} = 0.14$ to 2 d.p.

Test yourself

Draw possibility space diagrams for the following ways of using two dice. For each one, find the most likely score and work out its probability.

1 The score is the difference between the two dice (e.g. 4 and 1 scores 3).

2 The score is 1 for a double, 0 for anything else.

3 The score is equal to the biggest score showing on either die (e.g. 4 and 1 scores 4).

4 The score is equal to the smallest score showing on either die (e.g. 4 and 1 scores 1).

Probability

BBC GCSE Check and Test: Maths

Probability

When probabilities of outcomes that are not equally likely have to be combined, mathematical rules have to be used.

The OR rule

When two outcomes of the same event are exclusive, the probability that either one or the other will happen is the sum of the individual probabilities. If the two outcomes are called A and B, then $P(A \text{ or } B) = P(A) + P(B)$. This also works when more than two outcomes are involved.

The AND rule

When two events are independent, the probability that a given pair of outcomes from each event will happen is the product of the individual probabilities. If the outcomes from the two events are called X and Y, then $P(X \text{ and } Y) = P(X) \times P(Y)$. This also works when more than two events are involved.

Test yourself

A computer program for selecting National Lottery numbers uses these probabilities:

Numbers	1-5	6-10	11-15	16-20	21-30	31-40	41-45	46-49
Probability	0.2	0.2	0.15	0.07	0.12	0.12	0.06	0.08

What is the probability that the program will select:

1 A number that is 10 or less?

2 A number over 20 but less than 40?

3 A number over 30?

4 Two numbers in the 21-30 range?

5 Two numbers over 40?

6 Six numbers that are 10 or less?

Check the facts

In complex situations involving probability, it may be necessary to use both the OR and AND rules. A tree diagram can help keep track of the possible combinations. Tree diagrams have a group of "branches" for each event.

Example: A 10p coin has been biased so that $P(\text{head}) = 0.6$. A 2p coin has also been biased so that $P(\text{tail}) = 0.35$. What is the probability of flipping both coins and obtaining one tail and one head?

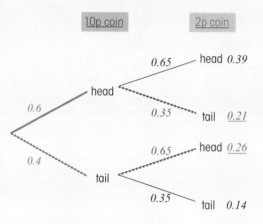

The two branches of the tree that give one tail and one head have probability 0.21 and 0.26. So the total probability is 0.47.

Test yourself

In each question, draw a tree diagram.

1 Irene is a careful cyclist and always stops at red traffic lights. There are two sets of traffic lights on her way to school. The probability of getting through the first set of lights without having to stop is 0.6, and the second set 0.4. Find the probability that Irene
   a) doesn't have to stop;

   b) has to stop at one set of lights but not both;

   c) has to stop at both sets.

2 Suppose that you have a bag containing various types of fruit. You know that in it there are three oranges, five apples and two nectarines. If you reach into the bag and pull out fruit at random, what is the probability that the first three will all be different?

Probability

BBC GCSE Check and Test: Maths

Answers

01 The four rules

1. a) 924 b) 161 c) 1058
   d) 145 e) 4560 f) 8.4
   g) 549 h) 1200 i) 2084
   j) 427 k) 1650 l) 9

2. a) 5615 b) 3975 c) 3816
   d) $893\frac{3}{7}$ e) 160 368
   f) 696

02 Types of number

1. a) $6, \sqrt[3]{1000}, 125, 1\,000\,000$
   b) $\frac{1}{5}, 0.3, 0.666..., \frac{7}{10}, 1.090909...,$

   $1.25, 1\frac{1}{2}, 6, \sqrt[3]{1000}, 12.5, 125,$

   $1\,000\,000$

   c) $-19, -0.5, 6, \sqrt[3]{1000}, \frac{75}{4}$
   $125, 1\,000\,000$
   d) $-\sqrt{12}, \sqrt[5]{10}, \sqrt[5]{10}, \sqrt{6}, \pi$

2. a) $4, 64, 729, 100\,000\,000$
   b) $11, 17, 27, 31, 51, 121, 131, 729$
   c) $2, 11, 17, 31, 131, 13\,331$
   d) $27, 64, 216, 729, 1331$

03 Powers and roots

1. a) 3125 b) 1 000 000
   c) 1225 d) 5.0625 e) 64

2. a) 27 b) 9 c) 1.2
   d) 1.710 to 3 d.p. e) −4

3. a) $10^3 < 2^{10}$ b) $\sqrt{625} = 5^2$

   c) $\sqrt[4]{100} > \sqrt[3]{31}$
   d) $2.1^5 > 2.5^4$ e) $(-6)^2 = 6^2$

4. a) $x = 12$ (b) $x = 3$
   c) Any value of x will satisfy the equation.

5. (a) 72 b) 32 768 c) 0.32

04 Index rules

1. a) 2^7 b) 5^4 c) 7^5
   d) 10^9 e) 8^6

2. a) 6^2 b) 9^1 c) 20^3
   d) 3^6 e) 4^6

3. a) $n = 5$ b) $n = 0$ c) $n = 2$
   d) $n = 5$ e) $n = 11$

4. a) x^7 b) c^4 c) p^5
   d) n^7 e) n^{a+b}

05 Negative and fractional powers

1. a) $\frac{1}{32}$ b) $\frac{1}{100}$ c) $\frac{1}{27}$
   d) $\frac{1}{5}$

2. a) 0.000 001 b) 0.0625
   c) 0.003 91 d) 0.0123

3. a) $\sqrt{5}$ b) $\sqrt[5]{100}$ c) $\sqrt[3]{2}$
   d) $\sqrt[9]{8}$

4. a) 10 b) 5.29 to 3 s.f.
   c) 0.2 d) 1.019

5. a) $\sqrt[4]{16^3} = 8$ b) $\sqrt[3]{125^2} = 25$

   c) $\sqrt[8]{5^8} = 5$

   d) $\sqrt[5]{100^2} = 6.31$ to 3 s.f.

   e) $\frac{1}{\sqrt[3]{8}} = \frac{1}{2} = 0.5$

   f) $\frac{1}{\sqrt[4]{81}} = \frac{1}{3} = 0.333$ to 3 s.f.

   g) $\frac{1}{\sqrt[3]{729^2}} = \frac{1}{81} = 0.123$ to 3 s.f.

   h) $\frac{1}{\sqrt[5]{10^2}} = \frac{1}{3} = 0.398$ to 3 s.f.

06 Rounding and estimating

1.

Accurate number	to nearest thousand	to nearest hundred	to nearest ten
6255	6000	6300	6260
15 640	16000	15600	15640
237	0	200	240

2.

Accurate number	to nearest whole	to 1 d.p.	to 2 d.p.	to 3 d.p.
1.6355	2	1.6	1.64	1.636
0.004 56	0	0.0	0.00	0.005
0.992	1	1.0	0.99	0.992

3.

Calculation	to 1 s.f.	to 2 s.f.	to 3 s.f.
$18 \div 7$	3	2.6	2.57
$\sqrt{200}$	10	14	14.1
1.25^5	3	3.1	3.05

07 Standard index form

1 a) 20 000   b) 700 000 000
   c) 1 500 000   d) 5 660 000 000
   e) 0.05   f) 0.000 000 8
   g) 0.0035   h) 0.475

2 a) 3×103 b) 4×107
   c) 6.5×10^2 d) 7.95×10^5
   e) 6×10^{-4} f) 9×10^{-8}
   g) 9.5×10^{-3} h) 4.24×10^{-3}

08 Calculators: brackets and memory

1 a) 192   b) 0.552
   c) 10.09495   d) 0.96
   e) 1.1   f) 12
   g) 113 050 000 = 1.1305 3 108
   h) 10.648

2 a) 8.763 243 243   b) 1.2
   c) −4   d) 2.9241
   e) 5.8   f) 4
   g) $500 000 000 = 5 \times 10^8$
   h) 131 072

09 Calculator functions

1 a) 5.477 to 3 d.p.
   b) 0.089 to 3 d.p.
   c) 5   d) 1.032 to 3 d.p.

2 a) −16   b) 0.9765625
   c) 5   d) 1.414 to 3 d.p.

3 a) $3 060 000 = 3.06 \times 106$
   b) 200   c) 199
   d) $70 000 = 7 \times 104$

4 a) 4.642 to 3 d.p.
   b) 15.708 to 3 d.p.
   c) 3.820 to 3 d.p.
   d) 50.265 to 3 d.p.

5 a) 0.940 to 3 d.p.
   b) 1.928 to 3 d.p.
   c) 85.325 to 3 d.p.

10 Equivalent fractions

1 a) $\frac{3}{4}$ b) $\frac{1}{2}$ c) $\frac{1}{3}$
   d) $\frac{4}{5}$ e) $\frac{8}{9}$ f) $\frac{3}{4}$
   g) $\frac{3}{5}$ h) $\frac{4}{5}$ i) $\frac{5}{8}$
   j) $\frac{7}{20}$

2 a) $\frac{1}{6} = \frac{2}{12} = \frac{5}{30} = \frac{10}{60}$
   b) $\frac{3}{8} = \frac{9}{24} = \frac{12}{32} = \frac{75}{200}$
   c) $\frac{180}{200} = \frac{45}{50} = \frac{36}{40} = \frac{9}{10}$
   d) $\frac{9}{36} = \frac{50}{200} = \frac{16}{64} = \frac{1}{4}$

11 Improper fractions and mixed fractions

1 a) $\frac{3}{2}$ b) $\frac{9}{4}$ c) $\frac{10}{3}$
   d) $\frac{45}{8}$ e) $\frac{27}{10}$ f) $\frac{41}{24}$

2 a) $3\frac{1}{2}$ b) $2\frac{1}{3}$ c) $2\frac{1}{5}$
   d) $1\frac{3}{8}$ e) $1\frac{17}{20}$ f) $5\frac{83}{100}$

3 a) true   b) false   c) true
   d) false   e) false   f) true

12 Adding and subtracting fractions

1 a) $\frac{5}{9}$ b) $\frac{2}{5}$ c) $\frac{7}{8}$
   d) $1\frac{5}{24}$ e) $\frac{37}{120}$

2 a) $\frac{7}{16}$ b) $\frac{1}{2}$ c) $\frac{13}{38}$
   d) $\frac{11}{42}$ e) $\frac{1}{6}$

3 a) $2\frac{3}{10}$ b) $1\frac{5}{12}$ c) $4\frac{1}{8}$
   d) $8\frac{7}{30}$ e) $1\frac{11}{40}$

4 a) $\frac{3}{4}$ b) $\frac{11}{12}$ c) $\frac{5}{9}$
   d) $\frac{3}{10}$ e) $\frac{1}{100}$

13 Multiplying and dividing fractions

1 a) $\frac{3}{20}$ b) $\frac{8}{45}$ c) $\frac{7}{16}$
   d) $\frac{2}{9}$ e) $\frac{4}{9}$ f) $1\frac{1}{2}$
   g) 5   h) 3

2 a) 4   b) 4   c) 4
   d) 3   e) 3   f) 6
   g) $\frac{1}{6}$ h) $\frac{7}{40}$

14 Fractions of an amount

1 a) £25   b) 40 grams
   c) 3.5 km   d) 12 cl
   e) 12.5 m^2

2 a) £135 b) 132 kg
c) 3.125 litres
d) 1 800 000 people
e) 45 ohms f) £31.35
g) 250 m
h) 3200 votes
i) 0.46875 cm
j) 47.5 tonnes

3 a) £100 b) 160 days
c) 100 km d) 10 hours 40 minutes
e) 200 cm^3

15 Percentages, fractions and decimals

1

	F	D	%
a)	$\frac{1}{2}$	0.5	50
b)	$\frac{1}{4}$	0.25	25
c)	$\frac{1}{10}$	0.1	10
d)	$\frac{1}{5}$	0.2	20
e)	$\frac{3}{5}$	0.6	60
f)	$\frac{13}{20}$	0.65	65
g)	$\frac{1}{8}$	0.125	12.5
h)	$\frac{7}{40}$	0.175	17.5
i)	$\frac{31}{50}$	0.62	62
j)	1	1	100
k)	$\frac{1}{3}$	0.333	33.3
l)	$\frac{2}{3}$	0.667	66.7

2 a) 22%, 0.235, $\frac{6}{25}$, $\frac{1}{4}$, 26%, 0.3

b) $\frac{5}{8}$, 66%, 0.666, $\frac{2}{3}$, 0.67, $\frac{27}{40}$

16 Percentages of an amount

1 a) £125 b) 54 kg
c) 4.5 km^2 d) 6000 people
e) £1.22 to nearest penny
f) 5200 litres

2 a) £250
b) 21.12 hours = 21 h 7 m 12 s
c) 125 cm^3 d) £3.75
e) 1.5 volts f) 121 kg

3 a) 4000 m b) 20 tonnes
c) 2.5 mm d) 1875 km/h
e) 3600 Mb
f) 5051 years to nearest year

17 Percentage changes

1

Julie	Malcolm	Serena	James	Mitchell
£16 275	£13 492.50	£8400	£20 637.75	£4725

2

New	1 year old	2 years old	5 years old	10 years old
£12 500	£11 000	£10 375	£8500	£4375

3 a) 25% increase
b) 5% increase
c) 20% decrease
d) 15% decrease
e) 4% increase
f) 10% decrease

18 Reverse changes

1 110 hectares 2 £12 000
3 39 m 4 25 years
5 12 200 cm^3 6 136 staff
7 0.648 m^2 8 5500 litres
9 21 kb 10 1300 seconds

19 Amounts in proportion

1 a) £2.50 b) 28 sheets
2 a) 3.78 kg b) 4 cm^3
3 a) 75p
b) 6.667 kg to nearest gram
4 a) 15.89 l
b) 2.20 gal to 2 d.p.
5 a) £3.36 to nearest penny
b) €1.64 to nearest cent
c) The graph should be a straight line, passing through the origin and the point representing €10 and £6.10.

20 Ratios

1 a) i) 1 : 5 ii) 1 : 5
iii) 0.2 : 1
b) i) 4 : 1 ii) 1 : 0.25
iii) 4 : 1
c) i) 5 : 6 ii) 1 : 1.2
iii) $\frac{5}{6}$: 1 = 0.83 : 1
d) i) 4 : 5 ii) 1 : 1.25
iii) 0.8 : 1
e) i) 20 : 9 ii) 1 : 0.45
iii) $2\frac{2}{9}$: 1 = 2.2 : 1

2 a) i) 250 m   ii) 2.5 km
       iii) 3.2 km

   b) i) 4 cm   ii) 60 cm
       iii) 4 m

3 a) $13\frac{1}{3}$ km   b) $1\frac{1}{3}$ km

   c) 18.75 min = 18 m 45 s
   d) 80 km/h

4 a) ii) $X = 5Y$ iii) $Y = 0.2X$

   b) ii) $X = 0.25Y$
       iii) $Y = 4X$

   c) ii) $X = 1.2Y$
       iii) $Y = \dfrac{5X}{6}$

   d) ii) $X = 1.25Y$

       iii) $Y = 0.8X$

   e) ii) $X = 0.45Y$

       iii) $Y = \dfrac{20X}{9}$

21 Proportional division

	Amount	Ratio (lowest terms)	Shares
1	£500	2 : 3	£200 : £300
2	160 kg	3 : 5	60 kg : 100 kg
3	80 ml	6 : 3 : 1	48 ml : 24 ml : 8ml
4	34.3 cm	4 : 3	19.6 cm : 14.7 cm
5	1331 sec	1 : 10	121 sec : 1210 sec
6	£1000	2 : 3 : 5	£200 : £300 : £500
7	60 km	5 : 4 : 3	25 km : 20 km : 15 km
8	2.8 g	1 : 6 : 7	0.2 g : 1.2 g : 1.4 g
9	350 t	2 : 5 : 3 : 4	50 t : 125 t : 75 t : 100 t
10	640 l	10 : 5 : 1	400 l : 200 l : 40 l

22 Scale drawings

1 a)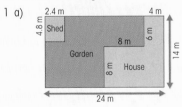

   b) i) 336 m²   ii) 120 m²
   iii) 11.52 m²   iv) 204.48 m²

2 All measurements are in cm.

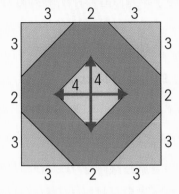

3 a) 1 : 50   b) 12.5 m

23 Inverse proportion

1 a) £7500   b) £62.50
   c) 200

2 a) i) 4 A   ii) 1.2 A
   b) i) 2400 Ω   ii) 12 000 Ω
   c) 6000 V

24 Substitution

1 a) 12.5   b) 22.5   c) −7.5
   d) 25   e) 4   f) 0.25
   g) 0.75   h) 25   i) 100
   j) 2

2 a) 125   b) 50   c) 350
   d) 12.5   e) 5100

3 a) 0.707 to 3 d.p.
   b) 1.732 to 3 d.p.   c) 0
   d) 30°   e) 60°
   f) 26.6° to 1 d.p.
   g) 0.966 to 3 d.p.   h) 1

25 Simplifying expressions: like terms

1 $12a$ 2 $3r$
3 $5s - 2t$ 4 $5y + 6z$
5 $7h - 4k$ 6 $-2x + 3$
7 $4n^2 + 3n$ 8 $4x^2 + 4x + 1$
9 $\dfrac{3}{u}$ 10 $\dfrac{c}{2}$

26 Multiplying and dividing terms

1 a) $12ab$ b) $2t^3$ c) $5f^2g$
   d) $6n^3m^2$ e) $24u^3v^7$
   f) $64i^2j^3$

2 a) $4x^2$ b) $\dfrac{b}{2}$ c) $\dfrac{5s}{2t}$

d) $\dfrac{2n}{5m}$ e) $\dfrac{3}{xyz}$ f) $\dfrac{5c^4}{6d^7}$

3 a) $\dfrac{2q}{r}$ b) $\dfrac{5}{t^2c^2}$ c) $\dfrac{4}{a}$

27 Expanding brackets

1 a) $2a + 2b$ b) $3a - 3b$
   c) $8a + 4b$ d) $30a + 50b$
   e) $-2a - 4b$ f) $-5a + 5b$

2 a) $u^2 + uv$ b) $2u^2 - uv$
   c) $3uv - 4v^2$ d) $2u^2 + 2uv$
   e) $10u^2 + 15uv$
   f) $-uv - v^2$

3 a) $x^2y + xy^2$ b) $8x^2y + 12xy^2$
   c) $-6x^2y + 3xy^2$
   d) $10xy^2 - 10x^2y$
   e) $xy^3 - x^3y$ f) $8x^3y^2 - 4x^3y^3$

4 a) $5p + 8q$ b) $11p - q$
   c) $14p + 6q$ d) $p^2 + 2pq + 2q^2$
   e) $4p^2 + 16pq + 6q^2$
   f) $-10p^2 - 15q^2$

28 Factorising

1 a) $4(e + f)$ b) $7(e - 3f)$
   c) $5(-e + f)$ d) $-2(2e + 3f)$

2 a) $w(w + z)$ b) $w(3w - z)$
   c) $w(4w + 3z)$ d) $z(w + 2z)$

3 a) $3A(A + B)$ b) $4A(3A + 7B)$
   c) $B(A - 6B)$ d) $-3A(2A + B)$

4 a) $pt(p + t)$ b) $4pt(p - 2t)$
   c) $3pt(2p + 5t)$
   d) $10pt(-2p + t)$

29 Products of two brackets

1 a) $ax - ay + bx - by$
   b) $ax + ay - bx - by$
   c) $ax - ay - bx + by$
   d) $4ac + 2ad + 2bc + bd$
   e) $2ac + 8ad - 3bc - 12bd$
   f) $10ik - 10il + 6jk - 6jl$

2 a) $x^2 + 5x + 4$ b) $x^2 + x - 6$
   c) $x^2 - 6x - 16$ d) $p^2 + 4p - 5$
   e) $a^2 - b^2$ f) $a^2 + 2ab + b^2$

30 Factorising quadratic expressions

1 $(x + 2)(x + 3)$ 2 $(x - 1)(x + 6)$
3 $(a + 3)(a - 4)$ 4 $(3x - 2)(x + 4)$
5 $(3x - 4)(2x + 5)$
6 $(4p - 16)(p - 2) = 4(p - 4)(p - 2)$
7 $(x + 4)(x - 4)$
8 $(2x + 10)(2x - 10) = (x + 5)(4x - 20)$
   $= 4(x + 5)(x - 5)$
9 $(6N + 1)(6N - 1)$

31 Simple equations

1 $x = 20$ 2 $d = -4$
3 $w = \frac{1}{4}$ 4 $B = 3$
5 $f = 8$ 6 $a = -2$
7 $j = 1$ 8 $y = 6$ or -6
9 $x = 4$ 10 $x = 5$ or -5
11 $n = 3$ or -5 12 $x = 89$

32 Rearranging equations

1 a) $y = 4$ b) $k = 10$
   c) $U = -2$ d) $d = 2.5$
   e) $N = 3$

2 a) $x = 5$ b) $r = -1$
   c) $x = 0$ d) $Q = 3$
   e) $v = 3$

3 a) $b = -2.5$ b) $v = -0.6$
   c) $s = -0.875$ d) $F = 5$
   e) $h = 3$

33 Equations with fractions

1 a) $x = 6$ b) $h = 10$
   c) $M = 12$ d) $d = 5$
   e) $s = 100$

2 a) $p = 11$ b) $z = 3$
   c) $f = 5$ d) $x = 3.5$
   e) $x = 2.2$

3 a) $a = \frac{1}{2}$ b) $e = 2$
   c) $x = 1$ d) $w = 1\frac{1}{4}$
   e) $w = 1\frac{1}{3}$

34 Trial and improvement

1 a) $x = 3.7$ or -3.7
   b) $P = 6.6$ or -7.6
   c) $y = 5.7$ or -3.7 d) $x = 2.7$
   e) $x = -0.1, -3.1$ or 3.2 f) $x = 2.3$

2 a) $x = 1.5$ or 7.5
   b) $z = 1.4$ or -3.4
   c) $n = -2.2$ or -0.1 or 2.2
   d) $q = 0.6$
   e) $p = 2.2$ or -2.2
   f) $a = 1.5$

35 Changing the subject of a formula

1 $A = B + 30$ 2 $r = \dfrac{d}{2}$

3 $n = 10(S - 5)$ 4 $h = \dfrac{t - 40}{2}$

5 $b = a - e$ 6 $p = \dfrac{f}{v}$

7 $y = \dfrac{3x - 5}{4}$ 8 $y = \dfrac{20 - 5x}{4}$

9 $s = r^2$ 10 $r = \sqrt{\dfrac{C}{3}}$

11 $u = \dfrac{4}{t}$ 12 $g = G - 100$

13 $b = \dfrac{a}{5}$ 14 $e = 3(f + 3)$

15 $p = \dfrac{q + 8}{10}$ 16 $h = \dfrac{V}{lb}$

17 $k = \dfrac{4}{m} - 5$ 18 $v = \dfrac{w}{3} - 1$

19 $y = (x + 1)^2 - 1 = x^2 + 2x = x(x + 2)$

20 $X = R + \dfrac{1}{2(Q - 4)}$

36 Functions

1 a) 100   b) 0   c) $\dfrac{1}{2}$
   d) 125   e) 1   f) 1.9
   (g) $\dfrac{1}{4}$ h) 1.331   i) 50
   j) 0.1   k) 27   l) 9

2 a) $f(x) = 4x - 2$
   b) $g(x) = 9 - x^2$
   c) $h(x) = \dfrac{2}{x}$
   d) $k(x) = (x + 3)(x + 1)$
   e) $C(x) = 1$
   f) $A(x) = \pi\left(\dfrac{x}{2}\right)^2$ or $\dfrac{\pi x^2}{4}$

37 Simultaneous equations: solving by elimination

1 a) $x = 5, y = 0.5$
   b) $p = 2, q = -3$
   c) $x = 4, y = -2$
   d) $a = 7, b = 6$

2 a) $m = -2, n = 4$
   b) $u = 7, v = 3$
   c) $L = 6, K = -4$
   d) $s = 0, t = 4$
   e) $x = 2, y = -6$
   f) $c = -1, d = -2$

38 Simultaneous equations: solving by substitution

1 $m = 7, n = 3$
2 $p = 5, q = -3$
3 $j = 4, k = -\dfrac{1}{2}$
4 $x = -1, y = 2$
5 $t = -2, s = -6$
6 $D = 7, E = -10$
7 $Q = 6, R = 4$
8 $f = -1, g = 1$

39 Simultaneous equations: solving with graphs

1 $x = 0.2, y = 1.8$
2 $x = -4, y = 2$
3 $x = 3.2, y = 0.6$
4 $x = 2, y = -0.5$
5 $x = 3, y = -7$

40 Inequalities and number lines

1 a)

   b)
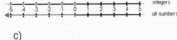

   c)
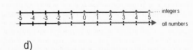

   d)

e)

f)

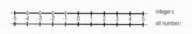

g)

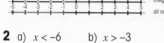

h)

2 a) $x < -6$ b) $x > -3$
c) $-1 < x < 3$ d) $2 < x < 4$

41 Solving inequalities

1 $x \leq 4$

2 $x \leq 1$

3 $x > 2$

4 $x \geq 0$

5 $x \leq -6$

6 $3 < x < 5$

7 $-1 < x \leq 0$

8 $-2 < x < -1$

No integer points satisfy the inequality

9 $x \leq -3$

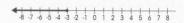

10 $-2 < x < 3$

42 Multiples, factors and primes

1 a) 1, 2, 5, 10
b) 7, 14, 21, 28, 42, 84, 210
c) 1, 4, 9, 36, 121
d) 1, 2, 3, 4, 6, 8, 9, 12, 18, 24, 36
e) 3, 6, 9, 12, 18, 21, 24, 36, 42, 84, 120, 210
f) 1, 2, 3, 4, 6, 7, 12, 14, 21, 28, 42, 84
g) 2, 3, 5, 7, 13, 29, 53, 127

2 a) 1, 2, 3, 4, 6, 8, 12, 24
b) 1, 2, 3, 4, 6, 9, 12, 18, 36
c) 1, 7, 11, 77
d) 1, 5, 25, 125
e) 1, 2, 4, 5, 10, 11, 20, 22, 25, 44, 50, 55, 100, 110, 220, 275, 550, 1100

3 a) Composite (3×41)
b) Composite (5^3)
c) Composite (3×7^2)
d) Composite $(3^2 \times 17)$
e) Prime

43 Prime factors

1 a) 18   b) 40   c) 42
d) 605   e) 286   f) 900
g) 928   h) 850   i) 891
j) 980 837

2 a) $2^2 \times 3^2$ b) 2×11
c) 59   d) 3×5^2
e) $2^2 \times 5^2$ f) 3×41
g) $2^4 \times 3^2$ h) 17^2
i) 23×29 j) $2^2 \times 167$

44 HCF and LCM

1 a) 5   b) 12   c) 9
d) 18   e) 30   f) 15
g) 21   h) 6   i) 25
(j) 27

2 a) 18   b) 30   c) 30
d) 105   e) 75   f) 144
g) 375   h) 168   i) 48
j) 60

3 a) HCF = 30; LCM = 4500

  b) HCF = 18; LCM = 5292

  c) HCF = 45; LCM = 6300

  d) HCF = 3; LCM = 730 626

  e) HCF = 1; LCM = 5 336 100

45 Number patterns

1 8, 10, 16, 32, 64, 66, 100, 126, 128, 210, 256

2 1, 10, 15, 21, 45, 66, 105, 210

3 1, 16, 25, 64, 100, 121, 256

4 1, 5, 15, 21, 25, 45, 63, 105, 121, 125

5 21, 63, 105, 126, 210

6 1, 8, 64, 125

7 (1), 5, 25, 125

8 (1), 8, 16, 32, 64, 128, 256

46 Linear sequences

1 a) 5, 8, 11, 14, 17

  b) 6, 16, 26, 36, 46

  c) 11, 10, 9, 8, 7

  d) 25, 20, 15, 10, 5

  e) 0.5, 1, 1.5, 2, 2.5

  f) 0, 1.5, 3, 4.5, 6

  g) −17, −28, −39, −50, −61

  h) 1.81, 2.82, 3.83, 4.84, 5.85

2 a) $T = 2n + 3$

  b) $T = 3n − 3$

  c) $T = 5n + 1$

  d) $T = 7n + 0.5$

  e) $T = 7 − 2n$

  f) $T = 10n + 8$

  g) $T = 0.1n + 3$

  h) $T = n − 5$

47 Quadratic sequences

1) $T = n^2 + 2n + 3$; 123; 10203

2) $T = n^2 + 2$; 102; 10002

3) $T = 2n^2 − 2n + 2$: 182; 19 802

4) $T = −n^2 + 3n + 1$; −69; −29 699

48 Other sequences

1 a) $T = \dfrac{n}{2n-1}$; $\dfrac{10}{19}$; $\dfrac{20}{39}$

  b) $T = \dfrac{2n}{2n+1}$; $\dfrac{20}{21}$; $\dfrac{40}{41}$

  c) $T = \dfrac{3n+1}{6n-2}$; $\dfrac{31}{58}$; $\dfrac{61}{118}$

  d) $T = \dfrac{n^2}{10n+1}$; $\dfrac{100}{101}$; $\dfrac{400}{201}$

  e) $T = \dfrac{8-n}{n^2}$; $\dfrac{-2}{100}$; $\dfrac{-12}{400}$

  f) $T = \dfrac{11-n}{3n+10}$; $\dfrac{1}{40}$; $\dfrac{-9}{70}$

2 a) $T = (2n + 1)(n + 1)$; 231; 861

  b) $T = (n + 3)(3n + 1)$; 403; 1403

  c) $T = n^2(5n + 4)$; 5400; 41 600

  d) $T = n^3(0.1n+5)$ or $\frac{n^2}{10}(n+5)$; 1500; 20 000

49 Metric units

1 a) × 100   b) ÷ 10

  c) × 1000 d) × 1 000 000

  e) ÷ 1000 f) ÷ 100

  g) × 100 000

  h) × 1000

2 a) 2000 mm = 200 cm = 2 m = 0.002 km

  b) 60 ml = 6 cl = 0.06 l

  c) 8 g = 0.008 kg = 0.000 008 t

  d) 480 mm = 48 cm = 0.48 m = 0.000 48 km

  e) 1 000 000 mm^2 = 10 000 cm^2 = 1 m^2

50 Imperial units

1 a) 225 g   b) 8 km

  c) 69 l   d) 1.27 cm

  e) 1.8 m   f) 1.425 l

  g) 348 ml   h) 75.6 kg

  i) 6.4516 cm^2 j) 1.35 kg

2 These answers are rounded to 2 s.f. where appropriate.

Answers

a) 0.039 in   b) 0.39 in

c) 39 in

d) 0.625 mi = 1100 yd

e) 0.036 oz   f) 2.2 lb

g) 0.034 fl oz   h) 0.34 fl oz

i) 1.75 pt   j) 11 sq ft

51 Accuracy of measurements

1 a) $7.5 \text{ cm} \leqslant x < 8.5 \text{ cm}$

b) $7.95 \text{ cm} \leqslant x < 8.05 \text{ cm}$

c) $14.5 \text{ kg} \leqslant x < 15.5 \text{ kg}$

d) $39.95 \text{ l} \leqslant x < 40.05 \text{ l}$

e) $495 \text{ kg} \leqslant x < 505 \text{ kg}$

f) $1950 \text{ m} \leqslant x < 2050 \text{ m}$

2 a) $12 \text{ cm} \leqslant P < 16 \text{ cm}$
$6.75 \text{ cm}^2 \leqslant A < 13.75 \text{ cm}^2$

b) $80 \text{ cm} \leqslant P < 120 \text{ cm}$
$375 \text{ cm}^2 \leqslant A < 875 \text{ cm}^2$

c) $27.4 \text{ cm} \leqslant P < 27.8 \text{ cm}$
$46.5625 \text{ cm}^2 \leqslant A < 47.9425 \text{ cm}^2$

52 Time calculations

1

Start	0:45:31	4:24:38	3:23:42	4:44:38
Duration	32:00	47:36	1:18:45	2:36:55
Finish	1:17:31	5:12:14	5:18:45	7:21:33

2 a) i) 41 min 21 sec

ii) 2 hr 17 min 50 sec

b) 52 cycles

3 365 days gives 31 536 000 sec.

53 Speed

1 a) 36 000 km/h   b) 2200 cm/s

c) 13.888... m/s

d) 259.2 km/h   e) 55 mph

2 Complete the table for these journeys.

Distance	Time	Speed
5000 km	2 hours	2500 km/h
1 km	$\frac{1}{4}$ hour	4 km/h
80 km	4 hours	20 km/h
400 m	5 seconds	288 km/h
43.2 km	1 hour	12 m/s
250 m	20 seconds	12.5 m/s
200 km	20 seconds	36 000 km/h
3 km	150 seconds	20 m/s
7 km	20 000 seconds = 5 h 33 m 20 s	35 cm/s
15 cm	$\frac{1}{10}$ second	5.4 km/h

54 Rectangles and compounds

1 a) $P = 45 \text{ cm}, A = 50 \text{ cm}^2$

b) $P = 4.8 \text{ km}, A = 0.8 \text{ km}^2$

2 a) 3.75 cm   b) 5.5 cm

3 a) 34 m2   b) 236 cm2

55 Triangles, parallelograms and trapezia

1 a) 120 cm^2 b) 9 mm^2

c) 73 m^2 d) 5.4 km^2

e) 6480 m^2

2 a) 24 m^2 b) 54 cm^2

c) 75 mm^2

d) 36 m^2 e) 40 km^2

56 Circumferences

1

Diameter	Radius	Circumference
12 cm	6 cm	37.7 cm
4 m	2 m	12.6 m
14 mm	7 mm	44.00 mm
3.18 m	1.59 m	10 m
12 400 km	6200 km	38 960 km
0.955 mm	0.477 mm	3 mm
124 cm	62 cm	389.6 cm
23.9 km	11.9 km	75 km

2 a) 59.9 cm

b) 177, to the nearest revolution

3 a) 5.59 cm   b) 20.1 m

57 Areas of circles

1

Diameter	Radius	Circumference	Area
10 m	5 m	31.4 m	78.5 m^2
8 cm	4 cm	25.1 cm	50.3 cm^2
4 cm	2 cm	12.6 cm	12.6 cm^2
4.14 mm	2.07 mm	13 mm	13.4 cm^2
7.14 m	3.57 m	22.4 km	40 km^2
6.68 m	3.34 m	21 m	35.1 cm^2
100 m	50 m	314 m	7850 cm^2
3.91 cm	1.95 cm	12.3 cm	12 cm^2

2 a) 1.57 m^2 b) 44.63 km^2

c) 16.1 cm^2 d) 4.07 m^2

58 Volume

1 a) 0.1008 m^3 b) 60 cm^3

c) $12 064 \text{ cm}^3$ d) 4000 cm^3

e) 2.09 m^3

f) $8.18 \times 10^9 \text{ km}^3$

2 191.52 ml

59 Surface area

1	166 cm2	2	600 cm2
3	152 cm2	4	15.7 m2
5	4398 cm2 .	6	2827 m2
7	360 cm2		

60 Types of formula

1	area	2	length
3	area	4	area
5	length	6	length
7	area	8	no dimension
9	volume	10	area
11	volume	12	volume
13	meaningless	14	area
15	area	16	mixed dimensions
17	volume	18	volume
19	length	20	mixed dimensions
21	length	22	volume
23	area	24	volume

61 Angles and lines

$a = 30°$ $b = 30°$ $c = 70°$

$d = 35°$ $e = 145°$ $f = 145°$

$g = 45°$ $h = 75°$ $i = 105°$

$j = 105°$

62 Parallel lines

1 a) $g = n$ (alternate)

   b) $c = o$ (corresponding)

   c) $k + q = 180°$ (allied)

   d) $i = p$ (alternate)

   e) $u + v = 180°$
     (angles on a straight line)

   f) $a = h$ (vertically opposite)

   g) $b = f$ (corresponding)

   h) $n + q = 180°$ (allied)

   i) $e = h$ (alternate)

   j) $h = l$ (corresponding)

2 $a = 112°$ (corresponding)

   $b = 68°$ (allied with a)

   $c = 68°$ (alternate to b)

   $d = 54°$ (corresponding)

   $e = 126°$ (allied with d)

   $f = 126°$ (corresponding with e)

   $g = 75°$ (corresponding)

   $h = 105°$ (allied with g)

   $i = 105°$ (corresponding with h)

$j = 75°$ (allied with i)

$k = 105°$ (allied with j)

$l = 105°$ (corresponding with k)

$m = 75°$ (allied with l)

63 Triangles

1	$x = 57°$	2	$x = 42°$
3	$x = 135°$	4	$x = 12.4$ cm
5	$x = 118°$	6	$x = 21°$

64 Quadrilaterals

$a = 65°$ $b = 115°$ $c = 115°$

$d = 65°$ $e = 90°$ $f = 115°$

$g = 123°$ $h = 123°$ $i = 57°$

$j = 57°$ $k = 50°$ $l = 130°$

$m = 83°$ $n = 82°$ $p = 155°$

$x = 4$ cm $y = 1.25$ cm

65 Angles in polygons

1 a) $1080°$ b) $1800°$

2   $a = 180° - 60° = 120°$

    $b = 180° - 45° = 135°$

    $c = 180° - 105° = 75°$

    $d = 720° - (120° + 132° + 90° + 135° + 105°) = 720° - 582° = 138°$

3 a) 7 (heptagon)

   b) 10 (decagon)

   c) 15 (quindecagon)

66 Regular polygons

1 a) $1080° ÷ 8 = 135°$

   b) $900° ÷ 7 = 128.6°$ to 1 dp

   c) $1440° ÷ 10 = 144°$

2 a) $360° ÷ 12 = 30°. 180° - 30° = 150°$

   b) $360° ÷ 15 = 24°. 180° - 24° = 156°$

   c) $360° ÷ 20 = 18°. 180° - 18° = 162°$

3

Interior angle	Exterior	Number of sides
140°	(40)°	9
(170)°	10°	36
(165)°	15°	24
157.5°	(22.5)°	16

Answers

67 Tessellations

1 a)   b) impossible

   c)   d)

   e)   f) impossible

   g)   h)

2 There are eight combinations of regular polygons that will tessellate. At each vertex, you can have:

2 triangles and 2 hexagons

a square and 2 octagons

3 triangles and 2 squares, in two different ways

4 triangles and a hexagon

a square, a hexagon and a dodecagon

a triangle and two dodecagons

a triangle,
2 squares
and a hexagon

68 Circle facts

1 $p = 113°$; $q = 86°$

2 $x = 18°$, so $3x = 54°$, $6x = 108°$, $8x = 144°$. Reflex angle = $12x = 144°$; angle at circumference in lower quadrilateral = $4x = 72°$; angle at circumference in upper quadrilateral = $3x = 54°$.

69 Pythagoras' theorem

1 a) 13 cm
   b) 28.9 cm to 3 s.f.
   c) 0.875 m
   d) 116 cm 3 s.f.

2 a) 15 m   b) 25 km

3 a) 5.39 to 3 s.f.
   b) 2.83 to 3 s.f.
   c) 25
   d) 2.40 to 3 s.f.

70 Congruent and similar shapes

1 a) congruent (SAS)
   b) similar (sides in equal ratios)

2 a) $x = 32.5$ m
   b) $x = 10$ cm $y = 12$ cm

71 Trigonometry: finding sides
All answers are rounded to 3 s.f.

1 $a = 7.21$ cm   2 $b = 22.3$ cm
3 $c = 14.8$ mm   4 $d = 3.53$ m
5 $e = 13.2$ cm   6 $f = 51.3$ m
7 $g = 3.48$ mm   8 $h = 7.07$ km

72 Trigonometry: finding angles
Answers are rounded to 1 d.p. unless otherwise stated.

1 $a = 68.2°$ 2 $e = 35.7°$
3 $b = 36.9°$ 4 $f = 29.0°$
5 $c = 30°$ 6 $g = 69.4°$
7 $d = 29.0°$ 8 $h = 33.6°$

73 Trigonometry: the sine and cosine rules

1 $a = 85°$

2 $e = 35.3°$
   $u = 22.1$ m to 3 s.f.

$f = 69.7°$
$v = 15.7$ m to 3 s.f.
$z = 6.69$ cm
3 $b = 86°$
4 $g = 127.2°$ to 4 s.f.
$w = 23.4$ mm to 3 s.f.
$h = 32.1°$ to 3 s.f.
$x = 20.5$ mm to 3 s.f.
$i = 20.7°$ to 3 s.f.
5 $c = 68.6°$ to 3 s.f.
$d = 53.4°$ to 3 s.f.
$y = 26.4$ mm to 3 s.f.
6 $j = 62.7°$ to 3 s.f.
$k = 36.3°$ to 3 s.f.
$l = 80.9°$ to 3 s.f. (NB: rounding causes
the angle sum to appear to be 179.9°)

74 Transformations: translations

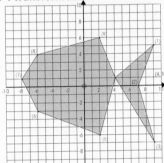

1	$(9, 5)$	2	$(7, 0)$
3	$(9, -7)$	4	$(4, 1)$
5	$(2, -6)$	6	$(-6, -3)$
7	$(-8, 1)$	8	$(-6, 4)$
9	$(2, 6)$	10	$(4, 1)$

75 Transformations: rotations

1

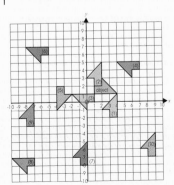

76 Transformations: reflections

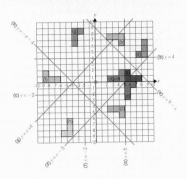

77 Transformations: enlargements

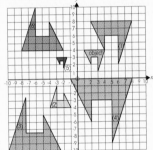

78 Constructing special angles

1 Check your own accuracy.
2 Check the result with a protractor.
3 Check that the sides are all equal
and that the angles are all 60°.
4 Check that the sides are all equal
and that the angles are all 90°.
5 Check that the sides are all equal
and that the angles are all 120°.

79 Bisecting lines and angles

1 a) Check right angles and that the
distance from each point to the
bisector is 5 cm.
b) Check that the two halves are
both 3.8 cm long.

2 a) 37° b) 14° c) 72°

3 a) Bisect a right angle.

b) Bisect a 60° angle.

4 Draw two points 6 cm apart and
construct their perpendicular
bisector. Set compass to 5 cm and
mark the bisector, using one of
the original points as centre.

Answers

80 Types of locus

1 With the sun as centre, you should have three concentric circles with radii of 2.9 cm, 5.4 cm and 7.45 cm.

2

3 a–b)

c) $PB = 3\frac{1}{3}$ cm

81 Combining loci: points and regions

1 a–c)

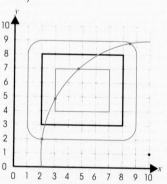

d) (2.1, 2), (3, 4.9), (4.7, 7), (8.5, 8.8)

2

82 Conversion graphs

1 a) i) £10 ii) £24
  b) i) £12.50 ii) £27.50

c) i) 50 min ii) 85 min
d) i) 20 min ii) 84 min
e) Dialmaster f) $33\frac{1}{3}$ min

2 Your graph should be a straight line, passing through the origin and the point (£50, $70).

$50 = £35.71, to the nearest penny.

83 Time graphs

1 a)

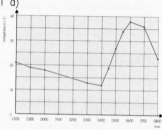

b) 0100: 16.4°C
   0200: 14.7°C

c) 0513 and 0728

2 a)

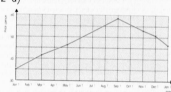

b) Feb 1: 38.5 p
   Jul 1: 52.5 p
   Dec 15: 48.5 p

c) June 5th, Dec 7th

84 Travel graphs

1 0740
2 20 min
3 40 km
4 0830
5 Carrington, for 10 min
6 Train A arrives at Benham station just as Train B is pulling out.
7 30 km/h

8

Attley to Dunsdale

Attley	(depart)	0730	1000	1400
Benham	(arrive)	0800	1030	1430
	(depart)	0820	1050	1450
Carrington	(arrive)	0900	1130	1530
	(depart)	0920	1150	1550
Dunsdale	(arrive)	1000	1230	1630

Dunsdale to Attley

Dunsdale	(depart)	0700	1040	1310
Carrington	(arrive)	0740	1120	1350
	(depart)	0800	1140	1410
Benham	(arrive)	0840	1220	1450
	(depart)	0900	1240	1510
Attley	(arrive)	0930	1320	1550

85 Plotting graphs

1

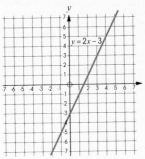

2

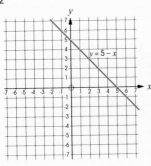

3

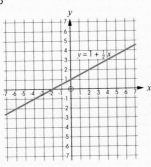

4

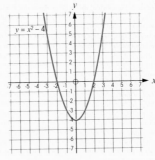

5

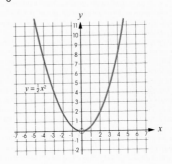

6

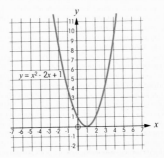

7

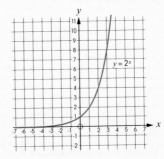

8

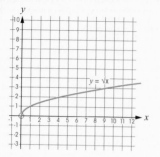

9

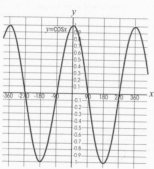

10

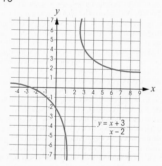

86 Gradient and intercept

1 a) gradient = 2; y-intercept = 3
   b) gradient = 4; y-intercept = –6
   c) gradient = –3; y-intercept = 1
   d) gradient = 1; y-intercept = 5
   e) gradient = 2; y-intercept = 0
   f) gradient = –5; y-intercept = 1
   g) gradient = –1; y-intercept = 25
   h) gradient = $\frac{1}{2}$; y-intercept = 1
   i) gradient = $\frac{1}{4}$; y-intercept = 0
   j) gradient = $\frac{2}{3}$; y-intercept = –4

2 a) $y = x + 4$ b) $y = 2x – 2$
   c) $y = –4x$ d) $y = 6 – 3x$
   e) $y = \frac{1}{2}x + 3$ f) $y = –0.2x – 1$
   g) $y = 2.5x$
   h) $y = \frac{1}{3}x + 10$

87 Inequalities and regions

1 a)

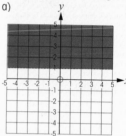

   b)

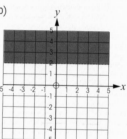

   c)

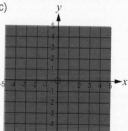

   d)

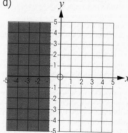

e)

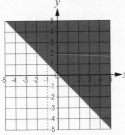

f)

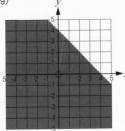

g)

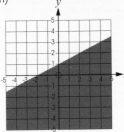

h)

i)

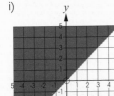

j)

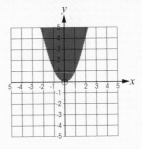

2 a) 32 square units

   b) 48 square units

88 Bar charts and pictograms

1 a–d)

Number of pets per student	Boys (a)	Girls (a)	All students (b)	Total number of pets
0	25	8	33	0
1	34	39	73	73
2	20	21	41	82
3	11	6	17	51
4	8	2	10	40
5	5	1	6	30
6	2	1	3	18
Total	105	78	183 (c)	294 (d)

89 Pie charts

1 The angles on the pie chart are:

Type of Plant	Flowers	Vegetables	Fruit Trees
Number of beds	160°	88°	112°

2 The angles on the pie chart are:

Job Title	Managers	Sales Assistants	Warehouse Workers	Drivers
Number of People	25°	170°	130°	35°

90 Scatter Diagrams

Note: the mean points and lines of best fit are marked on these diagrams.

1

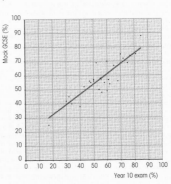

Strong positive correlation

2

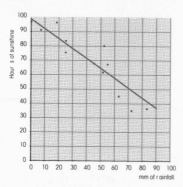

Strong negative correlation

91 The line of best fit

1 a) 35% or 36% b) 63%

Mean point = (55.4, 57.7)

2 (a) 64 mm   b) 78 hours

Mean point = (45, 68)

92 Mode and median

1 Find the mode and median for each data set.

a) Mode = 0; median = 1

b) Modes = 11.4 and 11.5; median = 11.4

(c) Modes = −2, −3, 0, 1, −4, 5 and 8; median = 0

(d) Modes = 304, 301, 298, 297, 300, 302, 299 and 289; median = 299.5

2 a)

Speed class	Frequency
$120 \leqslant v < 130$ km/h	16
$130 \leqslant v < 140$ km/h	7
$140 \leqslant v < 150$ km/h	6
$150 \leqslant v < 160$ km/h	4
$160 \leqslant v < 170$ km/h	3
$170 \leqslant v < 180$ km/h	6
$180 \leqslant v < 190$ km/h	3
$190 \leqslant v < 200$ km/h	5

b) $120 \leqslant v < 130$ km/h
c) $140 \leqslant v < 150$ km/h

93 Mean and range

1 a) Mean = 1.44 to 3 s.f.; range = 4

b) Mean = 11.35; range = 0.5

c) Mean = 0.714 to 3 s.f.; range = 12

d) Mean = 298.75; range =15

2 6.55 letters

3 a) 8 and 12

b) 5 and 15

c) {6, 12, 12}, {7, 10, 13} or {8, 8, 14}

94 Grouped data: estimating the mean

1

Parking time (min)	Frequency	MIV	Product
5–30	78	17.5	1365
26–60	125	43	5375
61–120	540	90.5	48 870
121–180	154	150.5	23 177
181–300	26	240.5	6253
Totals	923		85 040

Estimated mean = 92.1 minutes to 3 s.f.

2

Mark	Frequency	MIV	Product
20-40	2	30	60
41-50	8	45.5	364
51-60	19	55.5	1054.5
61-70	48	65.5	3144
71-80	73	75.5	5511.5
81-90	25	85.5	2137.5
91-100	12	95.5	1146
101-120	6	110.5	663
Totals	193		14080.5

Estimated mean = 73.0 marks to 3 s.f.

95 Grouped data: cumulative frequency

1

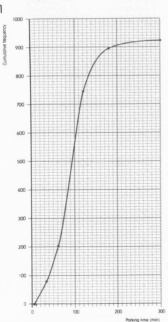

2

Median	Upper Quartile	Lower Quartile	Interquartile Range
95→72.5 marks	142.5→78.5 marks	47.5→64.5 marks	14 marks

97 Probability of a single event

1 a) $\frac{1}{4}$ b) $\frac{1}{13}$ c) $\frac{3}{13}$

   d) $\frac{1}{2}$

2 a) $\frac{174}{240} = 0.725$ b) 0.275

   c) $\frac{50}{240} = 0.208$ to 3 d.p

98 Combined events with equally likely outcomes

1

	1ˢᵗ die					
		1	2	3	4	5	6
2ⁿᵈ die	1	0	1	2	3	4	5
	2	1	0	1	2	3	4
	3	2	1	0	1	2	3
	4	3	2	1	0	1	2
	5	4	3	2	1	0	1
	6	5	4	3	2	1	0

$P(1) = \frac{10}{36} = 0.28$ to 2 d.p

2

	1ˢᵗ die					
		1	2	3	4	5	6
2ⁿᵈ die	1	1	0	0	0	0	0
	2	0	1	0	0	0	0
	3	0	0	1	0	0	0
	4	0	0	0	1	0	0
	5	0	0	0	0	1	0
	6	0	0	0	0	0	1

$P(1) = \frac{6}{36} = 0.17$ to 2 d.p

3

	1ˢᵗ die					
		1	2	3	4	5	6
2ⁿᵈ die	1	1	2	3	4	5	6
	2	2	2	3	4	5	6
	3	3	3	3	4	5	6
	4	4	4	4	4	5	6
	5	5	5	5	5	5	6
	6	6	6	6	6	6	6

$P(6) = \frac{11}{36} = 0.31$ to 2 d.p

4

	1ˢᵗ die					
		1	2	3	4	5	6
2ⁿᵈ die	1	1	1	1	1	1	1
	2	1	2	2	2	2	2
	3	1	2	3	3	3	3
	4	1	2	3	4	4	4
	5	1	2	3	4	5	5
	6	1	2	3	4	5	6

$P(1) = \frac{11}{36} = 0.31$ to 2 d.p

2

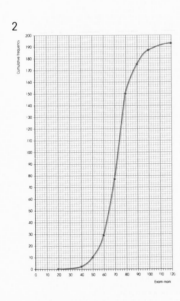

96 Grouped data: median and interquartile range

1

Median	Upper Quartile	Lower Quartile	Interquartile Range
461.5→87 mm	692.25→112 mm	230.75→63 mm	49 mm

Answers

99 The OR and AND rules

1 0.4   2 0.24

3 0.26   4 0.0144

5 0.0196   6 0.004 096

100 Using tree diagrams

1

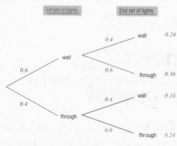

a) 0.24   b) 0.52   c) 0.24

2

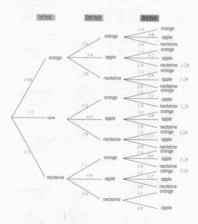

0.18